MB3

West of England
Market Towns

For all market people in town and country, in all weathers

Maggie Colwell

WEST OF ENGLAND
MARKET TOWNS

B. T. Batsford Ltd, London

© Maggie Colwell 1983

First published 1983

ISBN 0 7134 2780 9

Typeset by Tek·Art Ltd.
and printed in Great Britain by
Butler & Tanner Ltd.
Frome, Somerset
for the publishers
B. T. Batsford Ltd
4 Fitzhardinge Street
London, W1H 0AH

Previous page   View across to Selsey from below
Rodborough Fort. The church at Selsey in Gloucestershire
has fine stained glass by Morris and Co., some of the first
ecclesiastical glass to be executed by this famous firm.

Contents

Acknowledgement

I would like to thank all the kind people who stopped what they were doing to answer questions and assist with my research; especially all the helpful librarians, vicars, shopkeepers and auctioneers throughout the counties I visited.

In particular my gratitude to Francis Shergold, Squire of Bampton Morris Men; Mr Gingell of Wotton Bassett; Miss Aish of Bridgwater produce market; Mr Waldron, Stroud Museum Curator; Stuart Harrison, Thames and Chiltern Tourist Board; George Swinford, stonemason and owner of Filkins Museum; Master Weaver Richard Early of Witney; Roland Meredith, Vicar of Witney; the Lloyd family of Great Bedwyn; Penny Annand at the National Federation of Women's Institutes; Ros and Neville and the librarians of Gloucester County Reference Library; Corinium Museum, Cirencester; Mr Drysdale, Mr Smith and Mrs Kavanagh at the Gloucester cattle market; Basil Comely, architect; Lydia Apperley of Eastcombe; Mrs Warlock; Les Koole, farmer; David Boughton for taking me to see Fred Larkham and Mr Brain at Westbury; Mark Ovington and Roy Wade and their law libraries, Nan Brown for lending me books; Lynne Edmunds for initially encouraging me; my friends and family for bearing with me; and finally to Betty for her vigilant correcting and for typing the manuscript so beautifully; and to my husband for his continued support and long suffering ear.

Preface

Market days and fairs (the Latin word *feria* means holiday), set amongst the taverns and squares of small towns, have traditionally not only been days for the countryfolk's business, but occasions to hear news, listen to sermons, criticize the government, discuss current prices and generally let off steam.

Our family has a tale of a great-grandfather falling foul of market day revelries – his horse was swapped for a strange one, that, not being familiar with the route home, tipped his drunken rider into the river where he drowned – and most families have similar dark stories of relatives relying on well-trained horses to bring them home. Old words like 'market-merry', 'market-fuddled', 'market-fresh' are indictive of what went on.

Nowadays market days in England are probably less boistrous; but the milling crowds, the noise, the colours of the fruit and vegetables, the clothes swinging in the wind, the gypsies and hawkers, the livestock, the hundreds of different things for sale or to bargain for – are all aspects of market days that make them exciting, important parts of our heritage and bring variety into our pre-packed lives.

The west of England is an area impossible to define with any authority – to some people it goes as far as Worcestershire, others simply mean Devon or Somerset – therefore the boundaries of this book have been generously stretched to include places too good to exclude. On the other hand time and space have forced me to omit others quite as worthy.

The area covered is all of Gloucestershire and parts of Hereford and Worcester, Oxfordshire, Berkshire, Wiltshire and Somerset – rich agricultural lands with long histories of markets and traditions.

Some market towns have grown out of all proportion, and become unrecognizable parts of industrial centres. These I have left out – they need whole books to themselves. Instead I have tried to write about what I found in the smaller towns and villages, those that can easily be enjoyed in a single day.

Many of the places mentioned have markets, but some less established ones come and go and fairs are moveable feasts, so it is best to check days and dates with Tourist Information Centres.

As is often the case with travel books one finishes writing just as one ought to be starting, thus many fascinating bits of research had to be left unturned. I am not a historian but have tried to put each place in an historical context and show to what extent markets have shaped our towns and villages.

Our country is very rich in customs and traditions and architecturally marvellously varied. There is so much to look at and to enjoy.

Minchinhampton, Gloucestershire, 1982

'To market, to market,
To buy a plum bun . . . .'

Traditional nursery rhyme

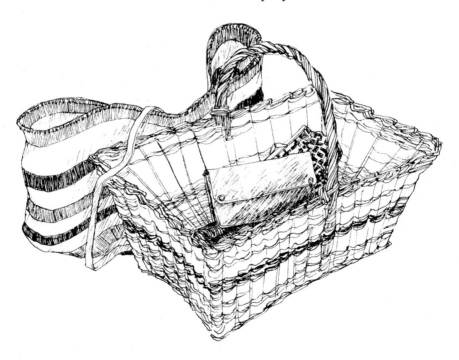

Introduction

A short history of markets and fairs

The Romans, just one of many waves of invaders to the British Isles, were people who left considerable legacies of buildings, main routes, place names and customs. Having established frontiers and quelled the natives, they set about creating beautiful cities in which to resume their elegant and well-organized lives.

Straight paved roads linked the colonies and towns that were planned around a grid system of parallel streets centring on a *forum* or market place. This large open space was cleanly paved and gave access to colonnaded shops, not unlike our modern shopping precincts.

The Roman forums appear to be the first organized markets that we learn of in Britain, and when these civilized people withdrew from the country, structured commerce disappeared as well.

The Dark Ages which came afterwards were lightened by the coming of Christianity. Monks were sent out from the centres of belief to travel about the islands spreading the gospel. Crosses were set up as meeting places for the small scattered communities of the hills and valleys. Gradually as the teaching spread, abbeys were established, Saxon kings built castles, and laws were made.

Because of the more stable times, people began to gather around the religious houses to celebrate saints days and holy days and the rulers held regular courts to settle disputes. Travelling was slow and often dangerous so a chance to take surplus goods to the ready-made crowds of the court hearings and saints days' gatherings was not to be missed, and travelling merchants liked using the security of the castle walls to sell their goods.

From these small spasmodic meetings and feast days our market and fairs evolved.

Gradually in Britain, regular commerce was established. People settled around the castles and abbeys and began to form communities. By the tenth century records show that market tolls were being taken and sent to the king, and when William the Conqueror invaded he found flourishing markets and fairs. Realizing that they were a source of revenue he set about organizing them properly.

Charters giving the right to hold a market and extract tolls were granted in quantity during the late eleventh, twelfth and thirteenth centuries; sometimes to recognize existing ones and sometimes to create new ones. Commercial expertise increased, foreign merchants came with oriental spices from the long established markets of the East, wine was imported from Bordeaux, pottery, silks and glass from the Mediterranean. The markets began to make the country wealthy.

Sovereigns gave market charters as favours to noblemen and knights who had served well in battle or proved worthy subjects, and lords of the manor guarded their rights jealously as the collected tolls went to them. Another market opening too close by ruined trade and thus affected their pockets.

Having originated in the monasteries and castles and because the new Norman churches were often the largest and most weatherproof buildings (and used for all sorts of activities – elections, payment of fines, storage of deeds and valuables, meetings, festivals) the church porch and the churchyard were natural places for the merchants to gather for trading. In 1285, however, a statute was passed forbidding fairs in churchyards and by 1448 the clergy saw fit to pass the Sunday Fairs Act – 'considering the abominable injuries and offenses done to Almighty God because of fairs and markets upon their high and principal feasts' – and Saturday was made regular market day. Trading was therefore pushed out of the porch and over the churchyard wall into the space beyond – this is why today many market places are next to, or near, the parish church.

As England prospered and expanded semi-permanent stalls were erected for use on market days ('shambles' for the selling of fish and flesh), official market houses were built for weighing and storing goods (sometimes including lock-ups and offices), and market officials checked the quality and quantity of merchandize.

Many good examples of these market houses exist in the west of England as well as numerous market crosses. These were sometimes single shafts with steps, or more elaborate structures canopied and pinnacled and offering shelter from the weather. Towns frequently had several crosses and they served as meeting places for differing trading businesses and also symbolized the market status of the town (which has come to be the difference between a town and a village).

Our present towns rarely follow Roman grid patterns, but have evolved and spread out from these original trading centres.

Area map.

MAP OF MARKET TOWNS

SCALE: 16 MILES TO ONE INCH

In the Middle Ages most towns were well served by markets. There were no permanent shops and the weekly gatherings around the crosses and market houses were important occasions for the household. Success depended upon the accessibility of the markets by the surrounding villages and hamlets and special roads were built. They exist today as 'portways' – *port* not in the sense of harbour, but meaning market town – originally a town with a gate. Portways can be found in many parts of England, and in the west one leads into Frome, Somerset; another from Bristol passes via Cranham into Gloucester.

Wide grass verges on the outskirts of towns sometimes signify drovers' routes leading into markets and fairs, street names in towns indicate their original uses – Horsefair, Sheep Street, Market Parade – numerous signs and legacies from our market past.

The west of England was (and still is) wealthy agricultural land well catered for by market towns, and parts of Gloucestershire, Somerset and Wiltshire have towns of obvious market origin often the statutory seven miles apart. This common law distance was stipulated by Edward III's charter in the fourteenth century. For an unmounted man, a reasonable day's journey was considered to be twenty miles. Divided into three parts – time to walk to market, time to do business and time to return home, 'And all these things it will be necessary to do by day and not by night on account of the snares and attacks of robbers' (Bracton in Pease and Chitty's Law of Markets and Fairs 1958) – results in six and two-thirds miles between markets, but it is commonly used as seven. Often it was many more, and countryfolk would set out before sunrise and return home by the light of the stars.

On a day-to-day level, markets were far more important in the Middle Ages than they are today. We have extensive modes of transport and deep freezes; they walked everywhere and food was seasonal and would not keep unless it was salted or dried. More time was spent on basic survival and the occasional feast day or fair must have come as welcome respite. Weekly markets brought in extra money to the farmers' wives for their poultry, butter and cheese, and animals could be fattened up for sale.

If the market floundered and traders stopped coming, the livelihood of the town suffered. Taking goods further afield to other towns was often unprofitable. Beasts that have travelled long distances are worth less and some animals just cannot walk far.

The Black Death of the fourteenth century wiped out whole communities and in the fifteenth and sixteenth centuries markets in some parts of England were on the verge of extinction. Some towns survived and went on to expand into thriving communities, others slipped back into small hamlets or even disappeared completely.

Sometimes kings and queens granted new charters to try and boost commerce. Those areas reliant on sheep and wool did not suffer as many areas did when foreign competition took the wool market. They turned to making cloth – to their salvation, as the big Cotswold wool churches signify.

The country had regained its strength by the time wheeled vehicles began to provide regular transport and the network of canals in the eighteenth century helped the internal importing and exporting of goods. Some markets lost local trade because of this increased mobility, but others gained strength and mushroomed.

Wealthy landowners began to replace the tumbledown medieval market houses and when the industrial nineteenth century spread to the west, covered market places with porticoes and steps sprang up and Corn Halls and permanent cattle sites filled the market squares.

The two world wars of the twentieth century caused many smaller markets to die. Governments organized central market places in the bigger towns to save energy and fuel, and when peace returned they were just never revived.

The wars also did much to alter the pace of life in the countryside. Scientific methods and mechanization came to farms, large herds of cattle were reared and bigger harvests gathered. The horse and cart gave way to motor vehicles and farmers began transporting animals in trucks and lorries.

In the 1950s and 1960s small cattle markets were removed from town centres and permanent purpose-built complexes erected on the outskirts. The big lorry parks and vehicular accesses have made it much easier for the farmers, but in some towns old-fashioned produce markets have been replaced by modern buildings which are not always so popular.

The holding of markets and fairs is controlled partly by custom and common law, and partly by statute. If a charter exists anyone can apply for planning permission and if granted start trading.

Happily in the last ten years charters have been re-established and stall markets spring up on empty sites and in car parks. Once again there is the likelihood of coming across the market bustle and activity in the centre of towns.

Markets granted by charters are very rigid affairs and although they can be bought and sold, the day on which they are held cannot be changed without permission from the monarch. Often the market of a town has remained on the same weekday for five or six hundred years.

Although few of the older ones apply now, there are special laws for market days. Courts of Pie Powder (*pied poudre* – dusty feet, i.e. travellers) were able to summon and fine on the spot in case the market day offender disappeared. Roads to and from markets had to be properly maintained and market days had to be advertised for the period of ten days prior to their opening. Any house beside the square could buy a licence to serve ale. Nowadays inns and public houses in the vicinity can ask only for extended drinking hours.

Markets also have a jargon of their own. The Jews who came over from eastern Europe – Russia, Poland, Romania – at the turn of the century to set up their businesses and stalls in the east end of London and necessarily speaking a mixture of Yiddish and English, peppered their market patter with native words – 'meshugena' for a crazy woman who can't make up her mind; 'ganeff' as a warning to other traders of a shop lifter. Nowadays London's east end markets have absorbed other foreigners and the Kosher butchers and stall holders are fewer, and Yiddish slang words only memories.

Similarly markets in Wales caught a smattering of Cockney dialect brought across on the produce trains and although tradition and long-standing market traders are diluted by younger and varied nation-alities, you can still hear the old slang in parts of England. A 'Toby' is the market official who allocates spaces and checks the length of the stall, collects the rents and regulates the types of goods sold – like the 'market lookers' of the medieval period. 'Lurkers' and 'standers' are the stall holders dealing in 'jacks' and 'flims' (five pound notes) and 'casers' the old five bob or shilling. On the smaller markets or more traditional ones, deals are sealed with handshakes or hand-slapping and 'a bit of luck' or 'luck money' can change hands especially at Christmas time. The person selling, or the auctioneer, gives the purchaser something extra as a symbol of a bargain or to encourage trade. Shouting out wares and prices is called 'pitching' and this is a skill still used by market traders everywhere. In the Midlands, the Birmingham Rag Market holds an annual 'Pitcher of the Year' competition and it is fascinating to listen to a good one in full swing. Some people object to the congestion caused by them but crowds adore the humour and entertainment they supply.

Feast days originated purely from gatherings associated with church celebrations or holy days and were originally separate from markets and fairs, having their own special traditions and ceremonies that often date back to pre-Christian times. Gradually feasts, fairs and markets merged and took on similar characteristics. So, in the early Middle Ages 'markets' and 'fairs' were similar occasions. Gradually 'fairs' emerged as more seasonal gatherings at road junctions, on common land or where boundaries met, whereas 'markets' were held weekly and always in towns or villages.

Many of the old fairs still hold an attraction for the same sorts of people as they did centuries ago. Townsfolk and countryfolk mingle together and at sheep and horse fairs you often find 'travellers' (gypsies) sometimes in their traditional barrel-topped caravans surrounded by dogs and goats. They use the fairs in the old way, to meet friends and family, exhange gossip and news – whilst the young girls show themselves off and the menfolk make sharp business deals. Great thick wads of notes exchange hands at these fairs and often you come across a couple of men behind sheds or between trucks, casually counting bundles of fivers and tenners.

Mop fairs have come to us from Elizabeth I's reign and the days of the landed gentry when their mansions needed armies of servants to run them and there was no newspaper advertising. Once or twice a year, generally in the autumn, those servants seeking a place lined up in the market square holding tools of their trade to show their skills and awaited employment. These fairs died away when social structures altered and newspapers carried regular advertising. They remain with us today mostly as pleasure fairs.

Women's Institute markets are always worth a visit. The societies aim to produce for sale, home cooked food, plants, vegetables, flowers, dairy produce and crafts, and the standards are always high.

Started originally to help the country in war time, the first real market set up as a business and working co-operative was in Lewes, East Sussex, in 1919. The next major increase was in 1932 when the Ministry of Agriculture asked the Women's Institute to distribute food to the starving and unemployed.

By the end of the Second World War there were 320 weekly markets and now there are 452 in England, Wales and the Channel Islands.

For 5p any man or woman can become a Life Member and Shareholder in their local Institute market enabling them to contribute produce for sale.

These markets expand all the time and are extremely popular. Held in church halls, old market houses or permanent market buildings and run by volunteer Women's Institute members, they always have mouth-watering displays of cakes and savouries, jams and pickles, and you have to get up early and join the queues if you want the best choice.

Somerset

Watchet Stogumber Crowcombe
Bridgwater Glastonbury Frome
Chewton Mendip Axbridge

Making the very western boundaries of the west of England, the County of Somerset has a coastline, hill ranges, marshes and pasture lands. The Mendips and the Quantocks stretch from the sea into deep valleys and low plains that have made good grazing lands since the West Saxon farmers brought their cattle here thirteen centuries ago. The Old English name apparently means the 'land of summer farm dwellers' and Somerset has been a rich dairy farming area right up until the present day.

On the Quantocks and the Mendips ran the sheep that made the merchants rich in the wool boom of the Middle Ages and by the nineteenth century the dairy produce had already enjoyed a long reputation. Farming methods have changed greatly, but in the times when all farmers' wives made extra money by churning butter and making cheese it was said that a husband was easily found for a Somerset girl who had a cool hand for butter making and a father with a good cider orchard.

It is still a farming community – both cheese and cider are produced and although many smaller country industries have disappeared, the towns enlarged and urbanized, the villages are as pretty as they ever were and the fishing ports on the long coastline have become popular as holiday resorts.

The Bristol Channel is busy with tankers and cargo ships bringing goods thousands of miles to the docks of south Wales, Gloucestershire and Somerset.

To the west of Bridgwater Bay, the town of **Watchet** has a large harbour at its centre. It still works as a busy port and you are quite likely to find ships from Pakistan and Portugal awaiting the tide.

A few hundred years ago when Watchet was a big important trading place, coal and slates were brought over from south Wales, and seaweed was taken up to the glass burners of Bristol. Iron ore mines on the Bredon Hills filled the sailing ships with cargoes and each tide was busy with traffic. Now it is tractors and car parts and cork and wine which are loaded and unloaded on the broad dockside, and the activity and bustle around the harbour makes Watchet a very attractive town in which to spend part of a holiday.

At the top of the cobbled slipway the old market house has recently been turned into a museum. Many of the exhibits are of course connected with the sea and several comtemporary paintings show the harbour enclosed by a wooden pier and there are old photographs of big dray horses pulling the lifeboat down to the water's edge.

Watchet's main street curves between the museum and a steamy corner café which still gives you a view of the sea on wet days. The shops are small and friendly and many have interesting Victorian windows. Although the beaches are not good for bathing, walks along the quays at high tide take you out into the sea, and on a warm summer evening it is a beautiful place to see the sunset. Later on the esplanade with its neat wooden shelters is lit with strings and loops of twinkling lights.

Behind the town there are tiny green lanes barely wide enough for a car and secret coombes full of calling birds and woodsmoke. Tucked into these folds are thatched cottages and some idyllic country house hotels. Beyond, the Quantocks rise up rather sparse and weather beaten, except for patches of heather and old twisted hawthorn trees. Around the edge of these hills is a frill of bright hamlets and villages with ancient stone churches and market crosses.

Stogumber – just off the main Taunton road – has a steep high street lined with colour-washed houses, and at the bottom a stream that once cured rheumatism and suppled local breweries still runs fast and clear. There are no buildings left from its market days, but at **Crowcombe** on the very edge of the Quantocks the market cross stands by the main road, its steps worn smooth by generations of use.

Somerset is well known for the wooden carvings in its churches and Crowcombe Church has a magnificent collection of exuberantly carved bench-ends showing interlocking vines sprinkled with flowers and bunches of grapes.

Opposite the churchyard is the beautifully renovated Church House built in 1575 to house the many activities that had been going on inside the church. When communites were smaller the church was the centre of village life and often the biggest and most solid building in the area. It was not just a place of worship and its uses were extremely diverse. As a large waterproof structure it often stored precious grain through the winter and acted as present-day village halls to house fêtes and seasonal plays. Traders used the big porches and children played in the churchyards amongst the vicars grazing sheep. Nowadays unfortunately churches have become rather silent and awesome places. They are, in their fabric and records, such interesting documents of people and past societies that it is a shame that the gaiety and life has gone elsewhere.

Bridgwater is right over the other side of the hills with the outskirts a bit harassed by main roads and motorways. The town itself is unspoilt and like Watchet it was a busy port as the River Parret (a tidal one with a twice daily bore) comes right through its centre. The quays on either side are lined with high wharf-like buildings with curly Dutch gables. Sturdy black bollards and railings run the length of the west side, big iron rings for tying up the boats are set into the walls.

The Victorians, as always, made good industrial use of the river and baked the river silt into oblong cakes. It became well known to housewives as Bath stone and was used to clean the front steps and scour household grates.

On the edge of the river old pubs and warehouses remain amongst the newer industrial estates whilst further into the town the chestnuts and copper beech of Kings Square and the many small roads with Georgian and Victorian buildings make Bridgwater a delightful mixture of river port and elegant town.

In the centre the statue of Admiral Blake and the dome and ionic columns of the Corn Hall mark the site of the original market place. Behind this rather grand façade is one of the best and most entertaining markets in Somerset. The inside is a little frayed at the edges but it is full of people and gossip and laughter. Many of the stall holders are local families who have been trading there for sixty years or more. Recently

Market House (now a museum), Watchet.

they banded together to resist a Council facelift, so behind the lofty pillars the turquoise paint is still peeling and the Victorian archways and alleys make it draughty in the winter. In spite of this it remains a busy, lively place with a jolly atmosphere that modern trading environments somehow do not foster. The main market day is Wednesday, although many traders remain all week. There are stalls selling farmhouse cheese, others piled with local fruit and vegetables, and there are socks, woollens, flowers and china. Shoppers mill about whilst traders call across the crowded gangways. At the back near the church entrance, old men lean on sticks whilst some weave about as the pubs in the vicinity of markets can – and often do – apply for extended drinking hours. This part of the market is also where the Wednesday auctions take place and during the morning the half a dozen trestles become laden with produce. There is a tremendous feeling of the country coming to town for the day, and some of the older folk have knobbly hands and weather-beaten faces; the women coming to do their weekly shopping carry big creaking willow baskets.

By lunchtime the trestles are piled high with wet cabbages and bunches of dark-earthed carrots. There

The high street of Watchet that leads down to the market house and harbour is lined with pretty Victorian shop fronts.

are baskets of blackberries or bunches of flowers depending on the season and often neatly trussed chickens and home-made pies – anything in fact that will sell and bring in a little extra cash. Alongside the garden produce there is a pile of secondhand household items, old bikes and lawn mowers and bits of furniture.

The auction starts some time after two o'clock and presiding over the noisy mêlé is Miss Aish, a stout pink powdery local woman with many years' experience of how to get rid of goods at the best prices. When she started nearly sixty years ago this back area was all poultry with the central part given over to vegetables and dairy produce. Now each week Miss Aish expertly auctions off the mixture of junk and home produce by popular demand in the old pound, shillings and pence currency. It is a fascinating experience to hear her quickly get rid of a secondhand bike for £8.10s.0d. or start the bidding at 17s.6d., and it is all well sprinkled with threats and admonishments to any of the boisterous crowd who dare talk or giggle.

After the noise of the market a visit to the church behind the Corn Hall is a quiet contrast. There is much good Somerset carving in this Parish Church and a splendid Jacobean screen removed from across the nave is now behind the choir stalls. Above the chancel arch you can still see the hooks that held the rood and the pulpit is dark, finely carved oak. Beyond the altar piece is an enormous, rather ugly oil painting of Christ's descent from the Cross. It is supposed to be the subject of another earlier auction having been taken from a French or Spanish ship in the mid-eighteenth century and sold by this method. Experts have declared it a masterpiece, but it seemed very out of scale beside the beautiful black oak carvings of the rest of the church.

Leaving Bridgwater you cross the low Somerset plains and the Kings Sedge Moor to **Glastonbury**. In the 1810s Henry James wrote very eloquently of this town in his travel book *English Hours* and it is still a gentle, quiet place with its ruins, legends and stories of religious men.

As a town it grew up as a direct result of the big influential abbey that started well before the Conqueror came to England. It developed into a centre of learning and knowledge until the Dissolution of the monastries in the first part of the sixteenth century.

The town prospered from the pilgrims who came to this hub of Christianity and in the High Street and

Produce at Bridgwater market.

Northload Street there are many beautiful and ornate medieval houses. The George and Pilgrims Hotel was rebuilt in the fifteenth century to accommodate all the religious visitors to the town and its façade is a framework of perpendicular stone panelling and its guest rooms full of four poster beds. The nearby market cross is a Victorian replacement of an older gabled one that used to stand at the junction of the roads.

Sometimes ruins are disappointing and require too much imagination but Glastonbury Abbey is not like that. There are walls, towers, arcades and many complete sides of chapels to look at and thus easily understand their former glory. The portions of wall and Norman arcading that are more devastated are softened and romanticized by the grasses and wild plants growing in the cracks.

Whoever ordered the destruction of the abbey during Henry VIII's Dissolution had enough good sense to realize that the Abbot's Kitchen was a useful building and let it stand. It is interesting to be able to walk into a very complete example of a monastic kitchen in the fourteenth century. The building is a curiously attractive shape being square at the bottom

Inside the Abbot's Kitchen, Glastonbury.

with a fire and enormous chimney across each corner; it then rises to a central octagonal lantern through which the smoke and smells from the big coal and peat fires escaped. The exhibition panels inside the building tell you what the abbot's guests would have eaten. The menues compare very favourably with the spartan single meals that the ordinary monks existed on. Poor food and cold quarters made the older monks ensure that a few of the winter months were spent in the infirmary where the food was better and the diet more varied.

Amongst the ruins of Glastonbury Abbey stands the well preserved Abbot's Kitchen. Over open fires in the corners of the building, the cooks laboured to produce fine food for the abbot and his guests. Needless to say, the monks' kitchen in another part of the Abbey sent forth much more austere frugal meals.

Abbey estates provided much of the produce to be cooked. The Fish House at Meare (in the middle of Sedgemoor) once stood in vast fish ponds that would have been kept well stocked; the great tithe barn on the outskirts of the town would have been full of wheat and barley. It is now empty, and quite cathedral-like in size; it is part of the Rural Life Museum of Somerset.

The Abbot's Fish House at Meare stands in what were the Glastonbury Abbey fish ponds. The house included living quarters for the fishermen and the ponds provided fish that could be eaten fresh in season or dried for the winter months.

Above the collection of farm buildings that make up the museum the famous Tor is visible, a long pointed barrow shaped hill that takes on so many varying moods – sometimes misty and shrouded softly with the pink of sunset or high, sharp and pointed on a clear summer's day.

Below it are the flat lands of Sedgemoor, laced with straight roads like causeways between the willows. Amongst the lines of trees are the peat fields, cut up like blocks of chocolate cake drying in the sun with bullfinches and herons dipping in and out of the ditches and dykes. Here and there are purple teazels left over from the vast acres that were once harvested and used in the wool trade to raise the nap of the cloth.

There are few signposts in this area and fewer people and houses, so it takes on a very passive, flat tranquillity which is well experienced by walking or cycling.

Shepton Mallet has a fine covered market cross and pedestrian shopping lane and some lovely walks behind the church to the small stream, but the centre has been ruinously tampered with and made so tidy, that it is preferable to go on to **Frome**, a market town near the Wiltshire border.

Old photographs show that Frome's town centre has not changed much in the last one hundred and fifty years and the street pattern is still essentially a medieval one. Its weekly market was recorded in the *Domesday Book* and it grew into a prosperous milling town with the expansion of the wool trade. When eventually the north of England cornered the cloth **market** with its fast mechanization, the Victorians used their business ingenuity to keep the town going where others fell into slumps and declined.

Up behind the market place of Frome are complete cobbled medieval streets with steps and alleyways up and down to the different levels, and rows of interesting old shop fronts and high mill buildings. The expansion of towns since the 1950s has often pushed the cattle markets out to purpose-built sites on the outskirts, so it is very nice to be able to enjoy a cattle market that is just off the main street, as it is in Frome.

On Wednesday mornings the roads and the bridge over the river are packed with noisy scuffling trucks, trailers and pick-ups, and by ten o'clock, the mooing and bleating passengers have been transferred to the corrugated sheds and numbers slapped on their rumps. The size of animal markets is very seasonal (local auctioneers can always be consulted to find the larger, more interesting ones), but there are generally a few cows or calves pushing each other about or fat, worried-looking sheep squashed into small pens.

Display outside a greengrocer's in Shepton Mallet.

Around the auction ring in any country town there is a good cross-section of local farmers and landowners. They lean on the rails in various old jackets and weather-torn coats and look very bored and disinterested as if buying something was the last thing they had in mind. Yet the animals do get sold and it is very pleasant to listen to the musical rythmn of an auctioneer in full swing.

On the other side of the parked trucks in Frome's cattle market there are two sale rooms that overflow with people and produce making it difficult to see what is for sale. Damp garden fresh vegetables and fruit fill one room and next door the second has trestles laid out with eggs, farmhouse cheese and freshly pulled poultry.

In a little yard across from the stalls prospective buyers can yank live geese and hens out of pens and poke and squeeze them, and quivering nibbling rabbits can be closely examined through wire netting. Amongst all this there is generally a pile of junk waiting to be auctioned off.

In the market square itself there are more street stalls with fruit and vegetables and clothes, and in the summer an ice-cream van with an exotic name trailing a long queue of children and shoppers. The Mr Paniccia who fills the cornets has a very English accent, but his grandfather was Italian and started the business in Cornwall after the First World War. The family have now been making ice-cream in the Frome area for over fifty years.

The big Parish Church of the town was much altered and remodelled by the Victorians but they did it very sympathetically. There are some beautiful nineteenth-century tiles on the floor of the baptistry showing draped figures and interlaced fish motifs. The surrounding dado is carved to represent the net that the apostles flung into the sea when they became fishers of men. From the church you can step straight into Gentle Street, a rather wide medieval street, and up into Christchurch Street. Between this main road and the market place is a whole labyrinth of ancient streets and connecting alleyways with all sorts of architecture ranging from humble cottages to expansive Victorian shop fronts and places of worship.

Frome Market Place.

Past Frome towards Glastonbury and the Mendips, the world-famous Cheddar cheese is recorded being made as far back as 1086. Many kings and noblemen valued the 'great and prodigious cheeses of Cheddar' which often required more than one man's strength to place on the table. Cheese making was a seasonal occupation and traditionally done by the farmers' wives. They found it a sensible way of storing their good summer milk yield for the barer winter months. Modern farming and manufacturing processes have made cheese available (and also tastless) all the year round, but at the Cheese Farm in **Chewton Mendip** they have been making it in the old traditional way since 1957.

They make about one ton of cheese each day using the milk from their own herd so that taste and quality can be finely controlled. Visitors to the dairy can watch many of the processes and buy cheese and butter in the farm shop. When the morning's milk has been heated and the curd separated from the whey, the dairymen and dairymaids chop and turn the yellow blocks of curd until they look like large breadcrumbs. Salt is added and working very quickly they wedge these 'crumbs' into moulds (4 lb is a small one and 56 lb a large one) and put it into a cheese press overnight. The next day the coarse cloth is removed, the rind made by bathing the cheese in hot water, and the whole then wrapped in a new cheesecloth. It is pressed for another day and then put into store for six to nine months, depending on the strength of taste required. Being made carefully in this old, well-tested way, the cheeses from Chewton Mendip taste just like the ones that would have been for sale in the Wells market place of a hundred years ago, when hundreds of tons of cheese came in each week from the farmhouses of Somerset. Now there are only ten places in Britain that make cheese in this traditional way but the marvellous taste and texture is well worth the finding.

Axbridge is a small town on the edge of the Mendips and on a high summer's day the small square dazzles with colour-washed buildings and the whole sky seems to pour down into its centre. On winter days the timbered houses are crisp lines against dark clouds. Medieval merchants developed this little Saxon market town and many of their buildings with overhanging storeys and deep doorways remain in and around the square.

On one corner is a three-storeyed grey and white merchant's house which is now a museum. You can

One of the many medieval streets in Frome, Gentle Street was named after Tudor resident William Gentle and is lined with sixteenth, seventeenth and eighteenth century residences.

see how the ground-floor was once lock-up shops and exhibits illustrate how little the square has changed. Old prints show the butchers' shambles once in the square and the museum has the Axbridge nail which would also have been out in the centre of the town for use by merchants testing that the money rang true when people paid 'on the nail'.

Another corner of the square is filled by the big fifteenth century perpendicular church with its ornate pinnacles and decorative parapet. Just inside the south door it is a surprise to see a cupboard full of bread. Since 1688 a bequest provides six loaves for the poor of the parish. The vagrants and the residents who used this 'dole' were required to attend church on Sundays and the bread was given out after the morning service, but now, with the changing pattern of worship, this is no longer expected.

The dole cupboard is filled on Saturday mornings and the loaves nearly always disappear. It is rare to find a bread dole still being practised as many have been dissolved into other more modern ways of giving charity.

Now that the main Weston-super-Mare road bypasses, Axbridge is again a small and peaceful town.

ADDITIONAL INFORMATION

Watchet

Watchet Museum – opening hours mid-May to end of September, Monday to Friday 10.30 a.m. – 12.30 p.m., 2.30 a.m. – 4.30 p.m., 7.00 p.m. – 9.00 p.m. (no evening opening in September), Saturday and Sunday 2.30 p.m. – 4.30 p.m., 7.00 p.m. – 9.00 p.m. Admission 10p adults and 5p children.
Tourist Information Office – Minehead – Market House, Tel. (0643) 2624.

Bridgwater

Market day – Wednesday (but many stalls in market hall on other days).
Some early closing – Thursday.
Admiral Blake Museum – open Tuesday to Saturday 11.00 a.m. – 4.00 p.m., Tel. Bridgwater 56127.
Bridgwater Guy Fawkes Carnival – Thursday nearest to 5 November.
St Matthews Fair – last Wednesday in September and three following days.
Tourist Information Office – Taunton – The Library, Corporation Street, Tel. (0823) 70479.
Women's Institute market – Friday 10.00 a.m. – 1.00 p.m.

Glastonbury
Market day – Tuesday.
Rural Life Museum – opening hours vary with the seasons, Tel. Glastonbury 32903.
Miracle plays in Abbey ruins – July and August.
Glastonbury Tor Fair – second Monday in September.
Glastonbury Guy Fawkes Carnival – mid-November.
Abbey opening times – vary with season.
Tourist Information Office – Northload Street, Tel. (0458) 32954.

Frome
Market days – Wednesday and Saturday.
Early closing – Thursday.
Frome cheese show – one day agricultural show in September.
Tourist Information Office – Glastonbury, Tel. (0458) 32954.
The town's museum – was in the throes of moving to Bridge Street so the Tourist Information Centre should be consulted.
Women's Institute market – Friday and Saturday 10.00 a.m. – 4.00 p.m.

Chewton Mendip
Cheese Dairy and Farm Shop – open seven days a week (closed Sunday p.m.).
Cheese making demonstrations – from about 11.00 a.m. onwards until the cheese is finished (about 1½ hours) Tel. Chewton Mendip 560.

Axbridge
No market
Early closing – Wednesday or Saturday.
Museum – April/September – open daily 2.00 p.m. – 5.00 p.m., Tel. Axbridge 732012.
Ox roast and Mummers plays – before Christmas.
Tourist Information Office – Cheddar – The Library, Union Street, Tel. (0934) 742769.

Museum in Axbridge.

Wiltshire

Bradford-on-Avon Ditteridge Devizes
Alton Barnes and Priors Marlborough
Great Bedwyn Wootton Bassett Cricklade
Ashton Keynes Malmesbury

The vales and plains of Wiltshire make it a wide open county of massive skies and green chalk downs divided up into enormous fields. During the year whole hillsides change colour with various crops and farming activities and from the motorway that chops through its northern boundaries there are stunning views across towards the Marlborough Downs.

In the Middle Ages it was a sheep county and writers as late as the eighteenth century talk of farmers owning two or three flocks with three thousand or more sheep in each flock, and during the big seasonal fairs, a hundred thousand sheep were sold or exchanged.

The western edge of Wiltshire touches the belt of limestone that swoops through England from Dorset to Lincolnshire making such attractive towns and villages. **Bradford-on-Avon** with both water and local building materials was a prime site for the Saxons to stop at and by the time the Normans got to that part of Wiltshire, there was a regular market, a good vineyard and two mills. Near enough to the sheep rearing downs, the town grew steadily to become one of the most important cloth centres of the country and it weathered the fluctuations of the wool trade right up to the nineteenth century with its fine white Wiltshire broadcloth.

Architecturally, there is much to see in Bradford-on-Avon because of its prosperous past, but parts of the town are inaccessible to cars, and walking is the only way of seeing some of the older buildings.

The original centre of the town and market site runs down the steep pitch of Market Street to the Swan. Then the road narrows before going out across the well-known medieval bridge with its chapel-cum-lock-up and beautiful green gudgeon weather vane. There is a good variety of shop fronts in the Shambles and up Silver Street, and the river bank is lined with high mill buildings from many centuries. Above the town the hillside is terraced and the cottages and small

houses are linked by ancient trade routes and long flights of steps.

Apart from the variety of domestic architecture there are two beautiful churches, one of them almost entirely Saxon. In an age when we value ancient buildings, it is strange to think that this small narrow church was so hemmed in and covered with ivy that its original use was disguised until the nineteenth century.

Whilst supervising repair on some old cottages near the parish church in 1858 the vicar, Canon Jones, discovered two carved stone angels. Walking on the hill above the town he took a good look at the various roof lines. Amongst the jumble of cottages he discovered the roof that had belonged to the nave and underneath the fabric of a schoolroom and staircase, the chancel and the porch of the Saxon church. It was restored to its ecclesiastical status in 1871 and is now declared one of the best preserved in England. Experts seem to think that it dates from the seventh century and escaped alteration by being discarded and forgotten very early on in its history.

The interior is bare, yet extremely beautiful with its narrow, high proportions and enormous blocks of stone that make the walls. Small windows and deep tall arches make patches of light and dark on the hollowed slab floors and its size reminds one that everything was so much smaller in those days.

Next door the Parish Church has had money poured into it by the wealthy merchants of Bradford and the two buildings make an interesting comparison.

From the churchyard there are passages leading to

The Town Bridge at Bradford-on-Avon. Two arches remain from the thirteenth century and the building in the middle was once a seventeenth century chapel. Later, used as a two cell prison, culprits inside were said to be 'under the fish and over the water' because the stone finial on the roof supports a splendid copper gilt gudgeon.

the water meadows and pack bridge at Barton Farm which forms a new riverside park with picnic tables and information about the wildlife. The enormous tithe barn was built about 1340 and is always open to the public.

The town has accommodated the centuries' changes very well and the river path leads back to a new swimming pool and a big car park which is very central to the shops and market place.

The market used to be held in front of the Swan in Market Street and was still in existence at the turn of the century (although the three-storeyed market hall had fallen down nearly a hundred years before and the timber sold for twenty shillings).

Now market day is Thursdays and held just across the Town Bridge under the rows of limes and copper beech near the river. Although it is only a small market, there is a good mixture of stalls – you can buy sandles or teapots and fruit and vegetables, and most weeks there is a fishmonger and a butcher. There is a stocky gent with an underwear stall who keeps everyone well entertained with rousing cries of his 'pitching' and also a tea and ice-cream van to revive tired shoppers and children.

From the stalls and trestles there is a lovely view of the terraced part of the town called the Tory. The word is Celtic for rocky hilltop and amongst the cottages at the top you can see how the hillside juts out to make steep foundations and cellars. On these different levels are long rows of weavers' cottages with the characteristic larger windows and at the highest level a more elegant line of miniature eighteenth century homes with columns and porches. Squeezed onto the narrow ledges the gardens overflow the

St Lawrence, Saxon church at Bradford-on-Avon.

bulging walls with tall hollyhocks and masses of old-fashioned plants – all very bright and colourful against the pale stone. It is a fairly rigorous climb to the top, but well worth it for the exhilarating views over the town.

There is no vehicle access in some parts and people have to use the long flights of steps that were the original pack-horse routes in and out of the town, and the little pilgrim chapel (much restored) at the south-west end would have been used by travellers on their way to Glastonbury.

The village of **Ditteridge** on the way towards Gloucestershire, or Avon as parts are now called, has its Parish Church dedicated to St Christopher, the patron saint of wayfarers, as it lies so near to one of the many Roman roads in these parts. Deeply scooped green lanes lead to the tiny village where the pathway to the Norman church is almost overgrown with lavendar, and before dreadfully misguided Victorian 'restorers' destroyed it in 1860, there was a colossal wall painting of the patron saint. It is a very early building, the chancel arch quaintly skew from many alterations and the steps to the altar almost completely worn through by centuries of use.

To the east of Bradford-on-Avon further into Wiltshire, **Devizes** is tucked between the downs and the edge of Salisbury Plain. It is a community which grew up around a Norman castle that guarded manorial boundaries, and a road map of the town clearly shows that some streets follow the old castle defenses. You can see how the town spread, outgrowing the triangular market area around St Mary's Church, and shifting to the new broad High Street that is the main street today. It was a popular town in the eighteenth century and the Bear Hotel was a very busy coaching inn with some thirty coaches pulling in each day on their way from London to Bath. From medieval times Devizes was a natural centre for wool and cloth and throughout the Middle Ages the town was an important trading place. Markets were much smaller in those days, but more vital to people's lives – few permanent shops were to be found in towns. There were generally separate areas for each sort of produce and probably several market crosses around which a particular item would be sold. Thus in Devizes, historians write of a Yarn Market and a Tanners Market and a Fish Market. It was a natural centre for wool and cloth and by the eighteenth century was supposed to have the best market in

England for corn, wool, cheese, sheep and cattle. The old Butter Market still stands near St John the Baptist Church and the neo-classical front of the Corn Hall with its statue of Ceres overlooks the market place. Now the old Butchers' Shambles holds a twice weekly stall market which also fills the wide street outside, and there is a small cattle auction in the Black Swan yard on Thursdays. The present and only remaining market cross was built in 1814 and is inscribed with a dreadful cautionary tale:

The Mayor and Corporation of Devizes avail them-selves of the stability of this building to transmit to future times the record of an awful event which occurred in this market place in the year 1753, hoping that such a record may serve as a salutary warning against the danger of impiously invoking divine vengeance or of calling on the holy name of God to conceal the devices of falsehood and fraud.

On Thursday, the 25th January, 1753, Ruth Pierce of Potterne in this county, agreed with three other women to buy a sack of wheat in the market each paying her due proportion towards the same; one of these women in collecting the several quotas of money discovered a deficiency, and demanded of Ruth Pierce the sum which was wanting to make good the amount; Ruth Pierce protested that she had paid her share and said she wished she might drop down dead if she had not. She rashly repeated this awful wish; when to the consternation and terror of the surrounding multitude, she instantly fell down and expired, having the money concealed in her hand.

At the end of the market place in Northgate Street is the tall red brick building of Wadworth Brewery. Towering above the shops and pushing out that sweet malty smell of beer making, the brewery has been working there for over a hundred years. Still making it in the traditional way the company deliver to the town pubs with drays pulled by Shire horses – much to the delight of local children and lorry drivers who always wave and toot.

Weekday mornings around the streets of Devizes you can see them backing expertly into tight yards or unloading the oak barrels deftly onto straw-filled 'bumpers'. The present stables in Northgate Street were started in 1974 and now there are four bay Shire horses to be fed and groomed each day. The draymen are very proud of their magestic animals and all the harnesses and vehicles are in immaculate condition.

Early morning deliveries to Devizes pubs by the Wadworth dray horses *Mark* and *Major*.

They have a brightly painted show wagon and special black harness for competitions and charity work.

In any weather it is such a pleasure to see them all set out in the early morning – trotting through the still empty streets and later on unruffled in the heavy traffic – always accompanied by that lovely mixture of tinkling harness and rumbling wheels.

Bishops Cannings is the small village outside Devizes where the Wiltshire moonraker legend is supposed to have originated.

In the last century when smuggling was an important part of life, contraband came up from Dorset on pack-horses and disappeared into the villages and farmhouses of the surrounding area. One night in Bishops Cannings locals were disturbed at their 'work' by the excise men and pushed the barrels of liquor into the village pond. When the law had passed on, they fetched their long hay rakes in order to scoop up the booty only to be disturbed a second time. The wiley villagers told the enquiring officers that

they were raking up the big yellow cheese pointing to the moon's reflection in the water. Laughing at the yokels' stupidity the excise men went away leaving the villagers to finish their night's work – thus people from Wiltshire are known as Moonrakers.

Bishops Cannings is the beginning of a string of interesting villages between Devizes and Pewsey. Here, just beneath Milk Hill, is the largest single field in Wiltshire and up on the side of Tan Hill is the Alton Barnes White Horse, the first of many in the county. Some of these horses are clearly defined and recently weeded (in past years the scouring ceremony was a time of raucous merrymaking being the leftovers from pagan festivities), some are practically indiscernible, and all vary in shape and age. But whichever one you walk onto the views are magnificent and the atmosphere and reason for their existence is thought provoking and awe inspiring.

At the foot of this Victorian one, **Alton Barnes** and **Alton Priors** are tiny thatched hamlets with old farms. The barns still bear medieval construction numerals and some of the walls are ancient cob ones (a mixture of earth and chopped straw). The two

Show harness and wagon, Wadworth Brewery, Devizes.

parish churches are across meadows linked by stepping stones, and two of the most delightful in the county.

Alton Barnes from the outside is mostly restored red brick, but inside is a Georgian three-decker pulpit, a panelled gallery and an exquisite modern pane of glass. In the window near the altar on the south wall of the church is a small diamond light showing old-fashioned pointed stooks on Woodborough Hill and in the foreground the modern circular bales. Engraved by Laurence Whistler it is in memory of a local farmer Aurther Stratton whose family have farmed the area for three generations.

By contrast the church at Alton Priors is mostly Saxon with an old scratch dial and a most unusual heavily engraved brass memorial near the altar.

North of Pewsey is the ancient town of **Marlborough** with a castle mound older than Stonehenge and one of the widest streets in England. Like Devizes this wide main street makes the market place and in the past would have been crowded with semi-permanent butchers' shambles, stocks and pillaries, and a Market House. The Victorians with their rather extreme attitudes to architecture pulled down the crumbling medieval structures and replaced the market hall with a rather austere red brick building that stands away at the east end.

The rest of the High Street is lined with very attractive tile-hung buildings. Many are eighteenth and nineteenth century, not because of a frantic tidying-up process, but because a series of devastating fires that swept through the town in the mid-1600s. The Great Fire of 1653 (declared a national disaster) started in a tanner's yard near St Peter's Church, flew up the north side of the street and consumed much of St Mary's Church at the other end. Situated in a wooded area, many of the buildings would have been

Market at Marlborough.

timber with roofs of thatch. Numerous workshops and small industries worked with open fires within the town's centre and people used tapers and coarse tallow candles to light rooms. There was always a danger of fire, and once started it would jump easily from one wooden building to the next.

Eventually in despair after the third big fire in Marlborough, Parliament passed an act forbidding thatch in the middle of the town.

You can see some of the remaining medieval houses by walking down the many passages and courtyards, and the old pent houses with the rows of wooden pillars still shelter shoppers from the weather. The fire did not reach Silverless Street and there are a few very old shutters on some of the cottages. This part of the town was the original market place, although now of course the weekly market uses the High Street.

In the Parish Church behind the Town Hall, the Norman beginnings are pink and fire scarred. A vast rebuilding scheme was carried out by the Puritans after the Civil War, so the inside is very square and plain. A corbel just inside the south door shows a crouching cat, supposed to be the church pet who saved her kittens from the Great Fire.

The church at the other end of the High Street was declared redundant in 1974 but fortunately escaped demolition. It is now used for craft markets and meetings, and the accoustics make it an excellent concert hall. It is proud of being the first redundant church to house a Tourist Information Centre.

Marlborough is a very pleasant town to shop in with small friendly businesses, and a very good butcher near the Town Hall sells Wiltshire hams and home-made pies. Half-way down the other side a draper's shop has a curious motto carved around the gable.

The town is only a mile from the great Savernake Forest, a beautiful area of beech and oak woods. Originally a much larger area of virgin forest, it was full of deer and boar for royal chases and commoners exercised age old rights to collect firewood. Over the years areas have been chopped down for ship building and vistas and avenues were cleared and planted. Now the forest belongs to the Marquess of Ailesbury and is leased to the Forestry Commission, so many parts are open to the public. Beech always makes beautiful woodland and attracts all sorts of wild life and plants. The best known part of Savernake is the Grand Avenue, four straight miles of beech trees, but on a fine day you can stop practically anywhere and find soft paths sprinkled with sunshine and roofed by ancient tall trees.

Through Savernake you come to **Great Bedwyn,** once the stronghold and metropolis of the Saxon king of Wessex. There are new parts to the town but basically it is a quiet thatched village with farmyards amongst the cottages and a canal running through fields behind the church. Once a market town, preaching probably took place on market days when people would gather around the cross still in the churchyard. It no longer has a market but many craftsmen seem to have made their homes there.

Over the canal bridge is a basket maker and side by side in Church Street are a wood turner, a garden furniture shop and a monumental stone mason – very convenient as the stone mason is also the undertaker and the wood turner makes the coffins. This sort of co-operation is quite a regular occurrence in small communities but the appearance of the stone mason's building and yard is definitely far from usual.

All over the office and workshops is the most amazing collection of monuments and wall plaques. Fixed to every flat surface are brightly painted headstones bearing curious inscriptions, old measuring devices, cautionary verses and odd epitaphs. Under the apple trees in the 'Pleasure Garden' (always open to the public) are sundials, monuments in the shape of aeroplanes, stone beavers, cats, horses and angels. Outside the corrugated workshop a fountain is surrounded by busts on plinths and to complete the fantasy, a pair of iridescent live peacocks dip and strut around the stones. This truly remarkable environment is the work place of the Lloyd family who have been making and restoring monuments for three generations.

The collection was started when the great-grandfather came back from the Great Exhibition of 1851 with 'a few bits and pieces' which he fixed to the wall and thereafter the collection grew.

The Lloyds still make commemorative statues and headstones, and also beautiful fireplaces from the vast store of coloured marbles and stones in their stock yard.

After this strange collection of memorabilia so bright and gay, the Pumping Station at Croften and the restored windmill at Wilton seem awfully staid by comparison.

On any road out of this part of Wiltshire around Marlborough you come across vast rolling downs and most lanes and main roads lead to stunning views. Off the fast Swindon A345 there are empty tracks over the hills to Aldbourne. Once a market town, it is now a quiet place with a flint stone church and colour-washed houses. It is only five miles over the Berkshire border to Lambourne.

This town also has a little square and in the middle a well-preserved market cross. Everywhere are reminders of the famous racing stables with jockeys in the supermarkets and horses skittering through the streets on their way to the practice tracks.

As is often the case, churches attract and record curiosities from the past, and the guide to Lambourne Parish Church tells of a William Bush who made a strange journey to London by 'Ayre, Land and Water', starting from the church tower by way of a strange pulley system.

Whatever the weather, the road to Kingston Lisle presents such an enormous expanse of sky; it is a wonderful sight either blue or grey. Tiny villages cluster around the edge of White Horse Hill with its prehistoric dolmans and near the M4 motorway the old green Ridgeway makes its lonely crossing along the top of the hills.

The road to Wootton Bassett runs over Hackpen Hill where one of the smaller White Horses can clearly be seen. The hill is crowned with trees which in the summer make a clump of rich dark green against the yellow and black scorched stubble. It is now common practice for farmers to fire the fields at the end of harvest, and although not much liked by nearby dwellings, it makes powerful patterns in the countryside.

Sometimes old market houses were left to decay as in Bradford-on-Avon and Marlborough, and sometimes they were renovated and rebuilt by benefactors or wealthy lords of the manor.

In **Wootton Bassett** the Market Hall standing on stone pillars has few of its original timbers despite its 'Tudor' appearance. It was completely renovated in 1889 by the local Meux family and given to the town at the turn of the century.

Wootton Bassett had always been the market town of the surrounding area. In the nineteenth century flagging trade was revived when a great monthly cattle

Cottage at Kingston Lisle.

market replaced the weekly charter market. The upstairs room in the Town Hall is now a little museum and there are many excellent photographs of the main street during these cattles markets.

At the beginning, animals were not penned and the beasts ambled about exploring their new surroundings and one photograph shows a large cow emerging from a solicitor's office.

Hiring fairs were not merely a romantic rustic notion devised by sentimental diaryists and authors, but a very efficient way of solving servant problems. In the 1830s Wootton Bassett started a twice yearly hiring fair that was extremely popular and successful having some 4000 applicants and onlookers on its first day.

Lining up in the market place, applicants registered with the market clerk and wore blue favours to show they were available. A gown piece for women and a hat

Fresh eggs for sale at the Wootton Bassett market. Despite its 'Tudor' appearance, the Market House is a Victorian restoration.

for men were awarded as merits for yearly good service by the town officers and it seems to have been a very jolly affair. Towards the end of the nineteenth century hiring fairs disappeared with the arrival of newspapers and better methods of communication.

The Second World War and the expansion of centralized markets at Chippenham and Swindon saw an end to the monthly auctions at Wootton Bassett but recently a little stall market has started again in the main street.

Before the railway and easier transport came to the town of Swindon, it was **Cricklade** that served a large area as a central market town and it still holds a big cattle and horse show in August, reflecting its agricultural roots.

Jubilee Clock, Cricklade.

The Swindon to Cirencester road follows the original Roman Ermine Street and there has been a settlement just off this road at Cricklade ever since it was laid in the first centuries AD. As modern heavy traffic by-passes the town, it is a friendly self-supporting community with local families still running the shops.

The old cattle market was held once a month and Mr Giles at the hardware store can remember being late for school on those days when the activity of farmers and the noise of animals being tied up and penned all along the High Street was much more enticing than the schoolroom. Crowds came into town on these days to buy and sell and to make use of the long opening hours at the inns – the White Hart where the auctioneer had his stand was the favourite market day meeting place.

The Thames runs across the end of the High Street and Mr Giles has an old photograph that shows ranks of stiff smart Victorians watching a mass christening in the river.

At the other end is the Jubilee Clock and the pinnacle of the Parish Church rises up behind the shops. It is a big church in a large churchyard – in summer very pretty with flowering cherries and dark copper beech. The old market cross stands in the corner by the schoolroom.

Village crosses vary in size, shape and state of repairs and those in towns are often gone due to increased traffic. In Ashton Keynes just outside Cricklade there are four – an unusual amount – dotted around the village and no-one seems sure of their original purpose.

Malmesbury has only one cross, but it was definitely erected to shelter produce and people on market days. It is an extremely elaborate octagonal structure topped by a crown-like lantern with small statues and stands in a small square near the remains of the Abbey.

The Abbey at Malmesbury was started well before the Norman Conquest and learned monks made it a literary centre. They wrote chronicles and built up libraries and spread literacy to travellers who passed by. Under the Benedictines' careful husbandry it became a rich and prosperous Abbey until the Dissolution.

In 1539, it was ignobly sold off to a local clothier for £1517.15s.2½d., who filled the nave with clacking looms. Since trade was bad it only lasted three years as a factory and was then presented to the town as a Parish Church. Despite the Abbey's chequered career, there are beautiful parts left (although most of the domestic buildings are in ruins).

The south porch of the Abbey Church is famous for its unusual elongated sculptures depicting principal stories from the Bible. Around the doorway the figures wear carefully draped robes like those at Chartres Cathedral and the combined detail and balance of design makes the whole quite exquisite. Inside, the building is sprinkled with witty carvings – by using binoculars you can see different medieval stone grimaces and little beech leaves here and there are thought to be a mason's mark.

In the vestry, stained glass shows some of the Abbey's benefactors, including Elmer the monk, who at the beginning of the eleventh century took off from the Abbey tower wearing a pair of wings. He managed about a furlong before landing badly hurt in a nearby garden. Sensibly the abbot forbade a second attempt.

The parvise or porch room has some of the old library on show with one of those querky Breeches Bibles where the modesty of the publisher clad Adam and Eve in 'breeches' instead of fig leaves.

From the ruins in the churchyard there are walks down to the river that encircle the town. It was a prosperous weaving centre until the eighteenth century and the running water gave power to many mills. There is an old silk mill over St John's Bridge and the Athelstan Museum in Cross Hayes shows some of the famous Malmesbury lace.

Mrs Annie Goodfellow, the last of the lace-makers, has recently died but she could remember being paid six shillings a yard for a piece of lace that took more than two weeks to make. There are often displays of this skill at the Cirencester craft market and when you see the fine thread and complicated patterns you can understand how a yard could take so long to make.

Malmesbury is a stone town standing amongst green water meadows and pasture lands and only just in Wiltshire. The stone tiles, limestone and dry mortarless walls are the usual building materials, and evidence of the nearness of Gloucestershire and the Cotswolds.

The Watching Loft, Malmesbury Abbey.

ADDITIONAL INFORMATION

Bradford-on-Avon
Market day – Thursday.
Early closing – Wednesday.
Gallery – Linfield Gallery, Church House, Church Street, Tel. 02216 6136.
Tourist Information Office – Bath – Abbey Churchyard, Tel. (0225) 62831.

Devizes
Market days – Thursday and Saturday.
Museum – open Tuesday to Saturdays, Tel. Devizes 2765.
Devizes to Westminster canoe race – Good Friday.
Devizes Carnival – end of August.
Tourist Information Office – Canal Centre, The Wharf, Couch Lane, Tel. (0380) 71279.
Women's Institute market – Thursday 8.00 a.m. – 2.30 p.m.

Marlborough
Market days – Wednesday and Saturday.
Mop Fair – Saturday before 11 October.
Mop Fair – Saturday after 11 October.
Croften Beam Engine – open Sundays from April to October, Tel. Burbage 810575.
Wilton Windmill – open Easter to October, Tel. Great Bedwyn 268.
Tourist Information Office – St Peter's Church, High Street, Tel. (0672) 53989.
Early closing – Wednesday.
Women's Institute market – Saturday 7.30 a.m. – 11.00 a.m.

Wootton Bassett
Market day – Wednesday.
Early closing – Thursday.
Museum – open Saturday 10.30 a.m. – 12.00 p.m. in old Market Hall.
Tourist Information Office – 32 The Arcade, David Murray John Building, Swindon, Tel. (0793) 30328.
Women's Institue market – Friday 10.00 a.m. – 12.00 p.m.

Cricklade
No market.
Cricklade Show – August.
Early closing – Wednesday and Saturday.
Museum – open Saturdays.
Nearest Tourist Information Office – 32 The Arcade, David Murray John Building, Swindon, Tel. (0793) 30328.

Malmesbury
No market.
Early closing – Thursday.
Athelstan Museum – open Wednesday, Friday and Saturday, 2.00 p.m. – 4.00 p.m.
Tourist Information Office – Town Hall, Cross Hayes, Tel. (06662) 2143.

Oxfordshire

Faringdon Bampton Witney
Chipping Norton Kelmscot

Each year at Buckland just outside **Faringdon** in Oxfordshire, they hold a big autumn ploughing competition, which is not only entertaining, but explains many of the activities and crops that you see in the fields throughout the year. The plough is also one of man's most important innovations which enabled the first nomadic hunters to settle and grow crops, thus starting the first hamlets.

At Buckland there are displays of early steam tractors, some of them most peculiar contraptions with pillion riders sitting on top of the plough. Then there are the heavy Shire horses, still faring better than machinery in wet weather and now being introduced back onto some farms, and there are displays of rural skills as well as the actual competition work to watch. Bright tractors pull special dressing weights behind the ploughs to turn the furrows into smart knife-edge points and it seems to be the speed which is the secret of straight regular ploughing. Those that pull slowly and regularly are the ones that make the best and straightest cuts.

Between Faringdon and Witney is the little town of **Bampton,** once better known as Bampton in the Bush, surrounded as it was by impenetrable thickets. It was always a market town overshadowed by its bigger neighbours but now it is well known for its Morris Dancers and it has a tradition of dancing that stretches back unbroken for six hundred years. Tunes and steps are handed down by word of mouth, rarely written down and so easily lost, but Bampton has managed to maintain the tradition for this very long period (although in 1959 they were down to four dancers). Folk dancing of this type goes back to pre-Christian fertility rites when young men blackened their faces, covered themselves with fluttering ribbons and thumped the earth to ensure good crops.

Nowadays the Bampton Morris Men are so popular that the streets are crammed with visitors on Spring Bank Holiday Monday and people book in advance to have the dancers perform in their gardens and thus bring good luck.

The men start early in the morning and dance their way around the town via pubs and gardens until finishing at the Eagle in the evening where other invited teams then perform. The Bampton Morris Men are simply dressed in white trousers and waistcoats and wear flower-trimmed bowlers and the traditional leg bells. There is a leader or Squire who organizes the dancers, a musician, a collector and a fool, and the fool has to be one of the best dancers so that he can act about without actually getting in the way. Peculiar to this group is the Cake-Bearer who goes about the crowd with a heavy sword and cake-tin. Again there is good luck to those who eat a piece. In the old days the family at the 'big house' provided the cake and a sword was actually thrust through the tin, but now it is a very simple ceremonial one in honour of 'Jinky' Wells, a local man who did so much to preserve the dancing tradition.

Bampton is very good at community activities and a Great Shirt Race dating back to 784 is held on Bank Holiday Saturday and in the autumn the gardens are full of ripening pumpkins for the Annual Pumpkin Competition. In the Christmas week, Mummers peform their peculiar tableaux in local pubs. The fair that fills the town in August, originally a charter horsefair, is now an amusement fair from Norfolk and it is curious to see the big mechanical arms of space riders outside bedroom windows and the narrow streets invaded by bright circular booths.

The town's market seems to have been lost in the 1780s and the market place rather taken over by a Victorian Town Hall and a horrid untidy petrol station, but in the High Street there is a wonderfully eccentric shop. Completely inside-out, this antique and junk shop spews its marvellous clutter all over the pavement, the inside being so stuffed with pictures, curtains, old material and cardboard boxes that the owner just has room to open the door and perch inside. The window of the shop is hung with rows of pretty plates and the sagging shelves on the pavement are loaded with all sorts of crockery and glass.

The ancient medieval bridge at Radcot a few miles out of Bampton is a remainder of the days when goods were all transported by donkey or horses and wheeled vehicles were rare. Parapets were often low to allow clearance for the packs that stuck out widely on either side of the animal, and at Radcot the walls are heavily scarred by later wagon wheels.

With their good sheep walks and vast downlands, Berkshire and the Cotswolds ranked as the best producers of woollen cloth in Europe for many centuries. Their broadcloth and kersies were famous everywhere. Envoys were sent from foreign courts and there was royal patronage in England.

Depending on the breed of sheep and its length of 'staple' or natural fibre, towns would specialize in different types of cloth. Oxfordshire was celebrated for its white broadcloth and **Witney** in particular for its fine blankets.

The blankets are still being made and their history is an interesting one.

The Windrush stream that passes through the town has qualities that give special whiteness to woollen fabrics and, as old Roman roads lead to London markets and Cotswold grazing is on the doorstep, it was a natural place for successful cloth making.

The story of blankets goes back to a Thomas

Fair stalls going up in Bampton.

The butter cross at Witney. Formerly a religious shrine it became a butter market after the Reformation, providing cover for the sale of perishable foods. The worn steps under the gables are the remains of the shrine.

Blanket working in Bristol. In 1320 he is supposed to have raised the pile on a piece of woven fabric to a new height and this type of cloth was then known as a 'blanket'.

During the reign of Queen Anne, Witney was granted a blanket charter to restrict competition and stabilize the quality. From then on many kings and queens used Witney blankets and the tradition was continued in 1981 when blankets were specially woven by the Early family for the Worshipful Company of Weavers to give as a wedding present to the Prince and Princess of Wales.

The blankets were white with a traditional border of indigo, yellow, red and green. Into the side of the blanket four narrow bars indicated that they measured 60 × 90 inches and weighed five pounds each. In the old days when the Early family exported blankets to the Red Indians a three and a half 'point' blanket had a barter value of three and half beaver skins.

The Earlys are a well-known local family that has been making blankets for eight generations. When they first started, the cloth was not produced in centralized factories, but wool merchants used outlying villagers as work forces. Each week carts were loaded with raw wool and taken off to the cottages where the women folk spun the wool (hence the term spinsters) and the men worked the looms. Many cottages around wool centres can be identified as weavers' homes because of the windows that are larger than usual.

The looms were enormous objects often placed so that light fell over the weaver's shoulder onto the cloth. As it took fifteen good spinsters to feed one hand loom, weaving cloth 100 inches wide was a slow process.

Trying to feed large families on meagre wages meant that the men barely left the looms for meals.

Mr Richard Early, now in his seventies, still has an old hand loom and used it to weave the Prince of Wales' blankets. Made in the 1800s the dark wood is scarred and polished by constant use. Mr Early's loom has a Kay's Flying Shuttle, an object often spoken of in history books where its relevance to us today may seem rather obscure; but to see the bullet-shaped piece of wood and metal shooting across the loom on its own with a sharp rhythmic slap and returned by the pull of an overhead handle, it is easy to understand

The Blanket Hall, Witney.

how the weavers feared it. A second man was no longer needed to send the shuttle back across the weft, so work force and wages were cut by half.

Nowadays one minute's work on a very modern automatic loom produces the same quantity as three hours at an old hand loom and the Earlys have indulged in several startling record breaking feats.

At the turn of the century they created a world record by using power looms to turn a sheep into a blanket in ten hours and twenty-seven minutes. In 1969 the family broke their own record with the help of a hundred and fifty Cotswold sheep and the same number of skilled crafts people.

Starting with a 4.00 a.m. shearing, eight hours and eleven minutes later the first blanket was wrapped.

Bale tombs at Witney. These graveyard memorials are very typical of the Cotswolds but actually have nothing to do with wool. Their name derives from imitations in stone of the metal hearses placed over the body of a noble person awaiting burial.

Some of the fifty made were then flown by helicopter to London. By the end of the same day they were displayed in stores in New York, Milan, Paris and London with notices explaining that the wool had been grazing on Cotswold hills that morning – an amazing example of twentieth-century transport and technology.

The town of Witney is itself a mixture of old and new with greens at either end and modern shop fronts jutting out between Georgian bow windows and merchants' residences. Attractive raised pavements are lined with lime trees and in the central area there is a market place, Town Hall, Corn Exchange and old covered butter cross.

The church end of the town is elegant and spacious with smart black lamp standards and a wide open green nearby. The big church has a marvellous graveyard behind it with very old bale tombs and exuberant Victorian lettering – some headstones still bare traces of colour that was once so fashionable on

The Town Hall, Chipping Norton.

memorials. At the other end of the town is the Blanket Hall which was put up in 1721 for the Company of Weavers to have their blankets weighed and measured in, and to enable a proper standard to be maintained.

The Oxfordshire countryside is right behind the heart of the town and from the butter cross a footpath leads across water meadows to the hamlet of Cogges. The tiny church is a gem with a wonderful procession of medieval stone animals playing musical instruments all around the walls of one of the chapels, and the Victorian lychgate bears a very nice biblical quotation.

Behind the church stands the barns, pig-sties and cattle shelters of the original manor and it has now been opened to the public as an excellent museum of farming.

Sometimes English place names directly reflect the origins of a town or village. The prefix 'Chipping' comes from the Old English word for market and there are many towns with areas called Chippings.

Chipping Norton and Chipping Campden, one in Oxfordshire and one a few miles away in Gloucestershire, vied with each other as important wool markets of the area.

Main highways converge on Chipping Norton bringing trade to the town, which is just what the thirteenth century lord of the manor had in mind when he developed the place. Now it has large public buildings that give it quite a grand air. The old green in the centre, where charter fairs and markets are still held, is now tarmacked and terraced and planted with trees, making a very attractive centre to the town.

Bliss Tweed Mill on the outskirts of Chipping Norton, sadly closed in 1981. The firm won international prizes with its cloth and the building is a lovely memorial to Victorian industry.

Narrow alleys and steps link the different levels and there are many interesting old buildings.

The oldest part of the town is away by the church and a row of almshouses in Church Street is very pretty in the summer when borders are crammed with colourful flowers and climbing plants wind around the doorways.

In times when the church was more important to all men, wealthy merchants secured a place in Heaven by building almshouses or adding bits to their parish churches. Much rebuilt by wool traders, Norton Church is full of beautiful, slender perpendicular pillars.

Although modern, the large window in the south aisle is quite in the spirit of medieval craftsmen with its jolly colourful panes of glass. It depicts the story of the creation with waves and bright round suns, zooming meteors and planets. The animal kingdom is represented by elephants, pelicans and giraffes as well as other more domestic creatures and children must have fun discovering all these objects during long services.

The porch is unusually hexagonal, with demons grimacing from the ceiling. If benefactors were generous these big wool churches often had large porches added to them. Public buildings were scarce and many local affairs were sorted out in these doorways.

In the nineteenth century Chipping Norton became famous for making tweed and the name of William Bliss was internationally known for this warm woollen fabric. Sadly the mill closed down in 1981 but there is a good view of the building from the Worcester road. Built with typical Victorian panache to emulate a country house, it stands in sloping pasture land with grazing black and white cows and chestnut trees. The tall chimney is a distinctive landmark and around the top of the mill is a fancy parapet with decorative urns.

A few miles from the town overlooking valleys and county boundaries are the Rollright Stones – a circle of ancient monoliths known as the King's Men. A group of 'Whispering Knights' stand close by and across the road in Warwickshire is the single big menhir called the King's Stone. Legends say a king who set forth to conquer all England was stopped just at the crest of the hill by a witch whose land it was, and who turned them all to stone.

The stones have stood for over three thousand years and have triggered off violent emotions in men, being in turn worshipped or feared. Fires have been lit against them in attempts to destroy them and yet there is also a whole book devoted to their praise and worship. Apparently they have powers and influence to unlock the innermost secrets of man's being and there are eerie accounts of journeys through chilly Cotswold nights to hear their laughter at dawn. Understandably the area is now closed between sunset and sunrise, but just before the sun goes down behind the pines the hard grey stones are tinged with pink and yellow, becoming serene and very beautiful.

Whilst some people concerned themselves with the transient inner life, the Victorians rushed about casting everything solidly in iron and thrusting machines into money-making industries. A group of artists in direct opposition to this financial attitude came together at the end of the nineteenth century to form the Arts and Crafts Movement.

They moved their base from London to Chipping Campden and their art invaded the most rural villages and towns of Oxfordshire and Gloucestershire.

The naturalistic Art Nouveau style that grew with them adorns many memorials and buildings all over the West Country as well as influencing the rest of Europe. Numerous older buildings exist today only because of these artists' care and attention; they not only restored and built, but also made the objects to furnish the buildings. Many houses and barns have carefully carved latches and handles and there are pieces of beautiful hand-made furniture and textiles in manor houses and village halls from **Kelmscot** down to Sapperton.

William Morris was of course one of the prime innovators of this movement, shifting his home to Kelmscot where he is buried. His tomb is very badly weathered but you can just make out stylized foliage creeping across the simple bale-shaped stone.

The part of Oxfordshire around Kelmscot has the characteristic limestone of the high wolds but is in fact a lowland that flattens out to the Thames Plain. The roads are straight, flat and deserted and in the early evenings the landscape is particularly lovely. In the late summer the farmers burn off the stubble with red bonfires sending up flashes of colour into the darkening skies and smells like burned potatoes hang in the evening air.

ADDITIONAL INFORMATION

Faringdon
Market day – Tuesday.
Ploughing competition – October.
Aldbourne Carnival – September.
Tourist Information Office – 8 Market Place, Abingdon, Tel. (0235) 22711.

Bampton
No market.
Charter fairs – weekend nearest 23, 24, 25 August.
Morris dancing – Spring Bank Holiday weekend.
Mummers – Christmas week.
Tourist Information Office (nearest) – Town Hall, Witney, Tel. (0993) 4379.
Buckland ploughing competition – early autumn.

Witney
Market days – Thursday and Saturday.
Cogges Museum – 18 April to 27 September every day 11.00 a.m. – 6.00 p.m.
Witney feast – First Sunday, Monday and Tuesday following 8 September.
Early closing – Tuesday.
Tourist Information Office – Town Hall, Witney, Tel. (0993) 4379.
Women's Institute market – Thursday 8.30 a.m. – 11.30 a.m.

Chipping Norton
Market day – Wednesday.
Early closing – Thursday.
Fair – 17, 18 and 19 September.
Women's Institute market – Fridays 9.30 a.m. – 11.30 a.m. Methodist Chapel.
Tourist Information Office – 22 New Street, Chipping Norton, Tel. (0608) 41320.

Hereford and Worcester

Evesham Ledbury Dymock Ross

From the edge of the Cotswolds near Winchcombe and Cheltenham you can see the Malverns and beyond the Welsh hills higher and wilder than any gentle limestone wolds.

Worcestershire and Hertfordshire were amalgamated in 1974 and became one county – Hereford and Worcester – but for many people they remain separate areas that border each other.

In a countryside of timbered houses and orchard slopes, the Vale of Evesham was linked to the Midlands by ancient trade routes between the Malverns and Bredon Hill. Salt ways lead up to the mines at Droitwich and the abbey and manors of the area benefitted from the dark fertile soil.

Evesham as a town began with Benedictine monks in the eighth century when a local swineherd called Eves was out catching a stray pig and saw a vision of the Virgin Mary. The Bishop of Worcester, apparently seeing it too, founded an abbey.

Monks have always been excellent husbandmen and, with hard work and skills, always brought out the best natural qualities of any area.

At Evesham the abbey was well organized and, as was usual, totally self-sufficient. There are fishermen, craftsmen, shoemakers and bakers recorded and their cellars were filled from their own vineyards.

The monks also cultivated orchards and were really the first market gardeners of this area which became eventually known as the 'Garden of England'.

During the expansion of market gardening in the eighteenth century as many as sixty horses left Evesham each day with carts laden with produce for the Birmingham markets, and farmers welcomed the coming of the railways so that perishable goods could be marketed. As well as the traditional apples and pears and soft fruits, new crops were introduced and the area is famous for its strawberries, sweet corn and asparagus.

The Vale of Evesham is lovely countryside when the springtime blossom covers the small fruit trees and in the later summer there is a mass of fruit for sale at the roadside.

Some farmers grow as many as twenty-five different sorts of plum trees and fruit sheds are full of types rarely seen in shops. Green 'Warwickshire droopers' sit next to the small, old-fashioned damsons, and yellow egg plums so good for jams have a delicate pinky bloom to them. Victorias, the queen of the plums, always sell well but as they crop in a very short time, you have to be quick to find the farm that is picking them.

The town of Evesham is a bright, noisy place with heavy traffic queuing past the timbered buildings in the centre, but behind the market place are quieter alleyways and old overhanging houses. Cobbles lead to the churchyard of the town that strangely contains two parish churches and a separate bell tower.

They are both contained within the boundaries of the old Abbey and the bell tower, which was just finished before the Dissolution, fortunately escaped destruction. It has a lovely perpendicular façade, and besides ringing each quarter hour, the bells ring out at nine, three and six with a different tune each day for a fortnight.

As one would expect in such an area, there are markets in Evesham most days and on Thursdays and Saturdays a horse-drawn produce cart stops in Merstow Green. Toby, a very friendly scewbald carthorse, is a great favourite with children of the town as well as those in the outlying villages that he visits the rest of the week; and in the summer he is very handsome, with ribbons and flowers threaded into his harness and around his ears.

In the High Street is a permanent covered market hall. Behind the small façade of the Central Market is a vast stallage area where you can buy almost anything.

Here in the 1900s there used to be a daily auction of

fruit and vegetables – a big affair with enormous quantities of produce changing hands. Now due to the pressure of the controversial Common Market, the growers in the area sometimes have trouble getting rid of their crops.

The Saturday open-air charter market is owned by the Council so when the Central Market was opened in 1968 they were able to charge a levy to their rivals. Market trading is still governed by rules and laws laid down centuries ago.

At first the new market stalls filled only the first covered part of the Central Market but now they have overflowed into the auction area at the back.

It is a very lively affair and in the summer months lots of gypsy fruit pickers come there to shop. These travelling people – always with creased sunburnt skins and long crinkly hair – are used to bartering but as local shopkeepers are rather more conservative, they come to the market where prices can be flexible.

Unlike shops, there are many different ways of selling in markets. Sometimes prices are written up and therefore fixed and these traders are called 'Standers'. 'Lurkers' hang over their goods with no prices showing and weigh up their chances with shrewd looks when a shopper shows interest.

The Central Market, Evesham.

Butcher's shop in the Shambles at Evesham. Close by the Abbey grounds in the centre of the town, there are many well preserved timber-framed buildings.

'Screamers' or 'pitchers' sell by rapid torrents of shouted patter and up in the Midlands there is an annual 'Pitcher of the Year' competition.

But new markets spring up all the time without traditions or customs so the more established places are likely to be better entertainment – although Evesham has a few 'lurkers' and a young boy on the fruit and veg. stall at the back does a good line in 'pitching' surplus greens.

The townspeople, aware of their interesting past, have made a small museum which is now run by the local historical society. The Almonary Museum stands near Abbey grounds in Vine Street – although it is doubtful whether the timbered building was ever the original Almonary which would have been built to give alms. (One tenth of the bread and beer produced by the monks was given to the sick and to travellers.)

In the museum old market days are shown in faded photographs with sacks of corn and big willow baskets full of fruit littering the market place. There are also some of the official corporation measures used to settle disputes during the day's buying and selling. Upstairs is a small collection of domestic objects not often displayed and some are very similar to our modern utensils. Less well known are two or three beautifully carved bone apple scoops used in the days before false teeth by older members of the household for eating apples.

The River Avon loops around the town with gardens and walks along its banks making it a very popular spot for tourists and locals. There are ferries to Hampton, and the upper river is navigable to Stratford and right down to Tewkesbury in the south.

The distinctive humps of the Malverns are often a hazy blue-grey in the distance across the Severn Plain, but close to they are rather bleak and bare. Locals say that if you look due east to the next range of hills after the Malverns you see the Urals in Russia, but a view in any direction from the top or from the town is spectacular.

Malvern is now the permanent site of the Three Counties Show, a big three-day agricultural event held in June.

It was started as a one-day affair in the streets of Hereford in the first part of the nineteenth century, gradually extending to two days and visiting various towns each year in Herefordshire and Worcestershire. By the 1920s the show was held in rotation in Gloucester, Hereford and Worcester until it moved to Malvern in 1958.

The hills provide a magnificent backdrop for all the activities of the show. There are rare breeds to see, prize beasts and poultry, displays of rural crafts, Women's Institute markets, sheep shearing competitions, trade stands and show jumping – giving a very good insight into the countryside and agriculture in these three counties.

Beneath the western edge of the hills is the pretty town of **Ledbury**. Very much a country market town, it has many timbered buildings making splashes of black and white in between the coloured façades of the pubs and old-fashioned shops. It must be a town that epitomizes a foreigner's idea of England.

In the wide main street (once narrowed by a row of shops) is the Feathers Hotel, an Elizabethan coaching inn on the old Cheltenham to Aberystwyth route. The front is a patchwork of black and white rectangles, overhanging levels and high, narrow gables. Inside the big hall with a low ceiling, panelled walls and open fire make it a very cosy pub and hotel.

Most of the streets in Ledbury have fine examples of timbered buildings – in New Street the Talbot has a low, deeply carved entrance under jutting windows and at the corner of the street the 'House on Props' is one of the oldest in the town. On the other side of the High Street is Ledbury Park, a vast tudor mansion built by a local family and when Ledbury was the scene of a small battle during the Civil Wars, Prince

Rupert made it his headquarters.

It was apparently market day when Colonel Massey and his soldiers were surprised by Prince Rupert. Wagons and carts were seized and upturned in the confusion and mêlée and a blockage made across the street. The battle raged down Homend and up to the church, where bullets are still embedded in the church door.

Church Lane that connects with the market place has changed little since this skirmish – probably because it was closed to carriages in 1746 and posts were put across the end. Each side is lined with low medieval buildings and one of the original butchers' shops from Middle Row has been reconstructed in a space half way up. Some of the red brick Georgian houses have minute courtyards and the Heritage Centre occupying the old Grammar School has very clear exhibits explaining Ledbury's development from a tiny Saxon village.

In the twelfth century the bishops of Hereford, realizing the financial benefits to be got from market days, obtained a charter from King Stephen and raised the status from village to town.

The Hereford Bull (public House), High Street, Ledbury.

Ledbury Market House still houses the weekly market. Goods are slung over the rails or piled on trestle tables.

In the nineteenth century a twice yearly fair was changed to a monthly cattle market which took place in Homend. Nowadays there is a permanent cattle market off Bye Street so the animals are no longer penned in the road.

Homend is a very interesting street. On either side there are lovely shell porches and bow windows and many narrow alleys that lead to back gardens and yards. A row of knife grinding machines stands outside one of the old market pubs and there are stable doors and old worn steps.

Many Ledbury shops display goods on the pavement rather like the Victorian shopkeepers used to, which makes a walk around the town much more interesting. The Curio and Crockery Shop with windows and pavement overflowing states a very modern attitude towards its merchandize – 'plastic and artificial flowers and shrubs are now made quite life-like. They do not attract insects, require little or no attention and will last for years and years.' Near the plastic-flower shop a fruiterers has a pretty coloured glass confectioner's sign and on the other side of the street the grocer's shop has some interesting old advertisements stuck to the tall narrow doors and windows. In amongst this jumble of shops and houses there are two Victorian chapels adding yet more colour to Homend as there is vivid green glass in the big red façades.

The little stall market on Tuesdays uses the paved part underneath the market house – the old wooden pillars and bannisters around the edge most convenient for displaying things for sale.

The upper storey was used at one time as a theatre for travelling players and the town seems to have attracted artistic and literary people. Elizabeth Barrett-Browning spent her childhood there (her unfortunate memorial being the rather nasty 'Tyrolean' clock tower and library building at the corner of the High Street) and John Masefield the poet laureate wrote long narratives about his home town.

Hops have been grown in Herefordshire for hundreds of years and when the Normans planted cider orchards they started a tradition for cider making which blossomed in the seventeenth century and is still continued by Westons at Much Marcle. Medieval vineyards are also recorded and now once again you can buy locally made wine from McKechnies in Ledbury. Three Choirs Wine has gained a good reputation as an English wine and it is really only the difficult and variable climate which holds it back.

Just over the border in Gloucestershire, near **Dymock,** at Fairfields Fruit Farm, Mr Day and Mr McKechnie have been building a vineyard for eight years. Red wine needs a warmer climate so they plant white grape vines down southern facing slopes. As the English climate is so unpredictable, the site of the vineyard is extremely important and the quality of grape juice varies from one valley to the next, depending on its temperature and shelter. Types of weather are critical at certain times in the crops development and it is the hours of sun and length of growing time before frosts force a harvest, that makes or breaks a good year.

As vineyards in England have no long traditions like Continental ones, the Fairfield owners welcome new technology and experimentation and many new vines from California are being tried out as well as different methods of pruning and training the plants.

Harvest time pressings have come a long way from treading feet. Now the grapes are sucked up into a long cylinder where a pneumatic diaphragm moves up and down forcing the juices into a trough below the machine.

In Herefordshire and Gloucestershire (and parts of Worcestershire too) cider was drunk from the cradle – with toast for breakfast before school, or heated with ginger stirred into it to keep out the winter cold. Apple orchards were part of the landscape and vast quantities of cider were consumed by farm labourers and gentry.

Less well known, and never becoming a national drink like cider, was the perry made in this West Midland area. It was very popular – some tasted like champagne – and most farms and estates made it, often giving it as part of the weekly wage. Pear trees have long life spans and trees of three hundred years of age or more can be found in the old orchards around the Severn.

A good perry is more difficult to make than a good cider and very little replanting has been done in Gloucestershire since commercial firms took over the market, but at Fairfields some perry is now being made along with the farmhouse cider.

After apple picking the fruit sheds at Fairfields are a marvellous sight – full of gigantic wooden crates full of knobbly Howgate Wonders and enormous Bramleys, and the sweet apple smell reminiscent of grandparents' garden sheds and attics.

Ross is back over the border in Hereford and Worcester and barely 'West Country' but a gateway town. To the north are Hereford and Salop, and the whole of Wales lies a few miles to the west.

Herefordshire with its characteristic pinky-red soil rears good cattle and sheep. Ross, perched on a headland, the River Wye curving around its base and surrounded by such good agricultural land near the Welsh border, has served the area with a busy weekly market since the *Domesday Book.*

Before modern transport, the Tuesday market saw all the surrounding lanes and roads crowded with farmers walking in their cattle or pigs and drovers with their large flocks and herds.

Drovers were very respected in the farming communities, being the most important of the long-distance travellers. They were entrusted not only with the wealth of vast numbers of animals but carried money, documents and brought news from the big towns to remote farmhouses.

There was continual seasonal movement of all sorts of beasts – cattle, sheep, even some pigs and geese –

generally to fatten the animals on rich lowland pastures before going onto a fair or market. Often the drovers were dealers as well and attended markets to realize some cash; the drovers' road from the centre of Wales, passed through Ross to Newent and then onto the regular big cattle markets of Gloucester.

Other people came into the markets by horse and there are records of two hundred or more horses being tethered in Ross on a market day. Peculiar characters appeared from the lanes and hedges and there are tales of quack doctors selling odd medicines, sword swallowers and escape artists entertaining the crowds. A strange woman called Mary Davies sold

fruit tarts from the cubby hole under the market house stairs, decorating the goods with a thin stream of watery treacle from an old teapot, and Sally 'Fine Morning' always turned up to sell her watercress although no-one knew where she came from.

Apart from the livestock sold from the streets and the butter and poultry sold from the now demolished Corn Exchange, many of the Ross shopkeepers set up splendid displays of their wares on market day. Pubs were open all day and by afternoon trading had slowed down to a leisurely pace. There are many stories of people's endeavours to reach home after a market day pub session, some finding space at the bottom of the

Market House at Ross-on-Wye.

carrier's cart, and others relying on their well-trained horses and the drovers to return the new purchases.

Market day has always been a day for letting your hair down and although some families lost husbands and fathers in accidents many lamented the coming of the motorcar that needed to be driven.

This cross in Ross churchyard bears the inscription 'Plague Ane Dom. 1637 Burials 315. Libera nos Domine', a dreadful year for Ross when many fled from the town to escape the sickness. The dead were buried in a communal pit to the west of the cross, an area not used since.

In Ross now there is a big permanent cattle market at the bottom of Eddie Cross Street and in the centre, heavy traffic squeezes past the sandstone market hall, where on Thursdays and Saturdays a stall market sprawls out under the fat red columns.

Away from the bustle of the centre, the Close and churchyard are quiet and peaceful retreats. Inside the church, one of the big gothic windows is partially covered by virginia creepers.

In 1684 John Kyle, the great benefactor of Ross, planted some trees in the churchyard. They ran suckers up into the north aisle and two tall saplings

grew in front of the window until Victorian restoration removed them. Now as a reminder of this strange feature the creepers planted in stone troughs are trained up in front of the lights.

John Kyle also built a public garden around the church and from the Prospect you can look over the river.

The Wye makes some spectacular scenery as it winds down to meet the Severn estuary and in the eighteenth century it was a popular river for gentle dalliance and romantic atmosphere.

In 1745 the worldly Reverend John Egerton saw a unique way of entertaining his wealthy friends and he built a pleasure boat to take them to Monmouth and Chepstow. News of all this breath-taking scenery spread fast and Ross became very fashionable. The Royal Hotel was built to accommodate all the visitors and from Wilton Bridge, the round towers and arrow slits are 'Gothic' structures that were added during this period of 'chic' nostalgia.

Further into the town there are gazeboes, studded doors, spurious fire insurance signs and solid buttresses beneath castle windows – but they are all part of this sham, and affectionately known as 'Ross Romantic'.

The Wye no longer has steam ships or coracles, but when rowing gained popularity in the 1900s, the Ross Regatta became an important annual event, second only to Henley. Teams now came from all over Britain to take part in this one day event held on August Bank Holiday.

Below Ross, the Wye marks the border between Hereford and Gloucestershire, and on the Herefordshire side the river with one of its characteristic twists isolates a narrow neck of land above which is a craggy outcrop of rock called Symonds Yat. This is one of the best viewing points along the river and the path through the woodland and the stones at the summit are worn smooth by years of tourists. Despite this the view never loses its drama and its beauty.

You can look straight out to the wooded hills near Goodrich Castle and the spire of Ross Church or four hundred feet below miniature cows graze on the water meadows of the wide river. As with many Forestry Commission tourist sites, the facilities are good and information boards clear and easy to follow.

ADDITIONAL INFORMATION

Evesham
Market days – Tuesday, Thursday, Friday and Saturday.
Museum – open Good Friday to end of September, Tuesday, Thursday, Friday and Saturday and all Bank Holidays 10.00 a.m. – 5.00 p.m. and Sundays 2.00 p.m. – 5.00 p.m.
Tourist Information Office – Pershore Council Offices, Tel. (03865) 4711.
Early closing – Wednesday.

Ledbury
Market days – Tuesday and Wednesday (cattle only), and Saturday.
Heritage Centre – open seven days a week, Whitsun until end of September.
Early closing day – Wednesday.
Tourist Information Office – St Katherines, High Street, Ledbury, Tel. (0531) 2461.
Three Counties Show – Malvern – in June for three days, Tel. (06845) 61731.
Women's Institute market – Friday 10.00 a.m. – 12.00 p.m.

Ross
Market days – Thursday and Saturday (Friday for cattle).
Early closing – Wednesday.
Ross Regatta – August Bank Holiday.
Tourist Information Office – 20 Broad Street, Tel. (0989) 62768.
Women's Institute market – Saturday 8.30 a.m. – 12.00 p.m.

Gloucestershire and Avon

Forest of Dean Newnham Frampton-on-Severn Tewkesbury
Winchcombe Chipping Campden Moreton-in-Marsh Stow-on-the-Wold
Lechlade Filkins Northleach Cirencester Stroud Valleys Gloucester Tetbury
Wotton-under-Edge Tormarton Marshfield St Catherine's

The varied geology and geography of Gloucestershire, its positioning near to Wales and central parts of England, invited settlers from the earliest times. It is crossed and recrossed by ancient ridge tracks, saltways, portways, Roman roads and drovers' tracks. The Iron Age people mined and the Celts and Saxons built homesteads in the more sheltered parts; the Romans forded the rivers and built highways across the hills. The good farming land attracted many monasteries and religious houses giving rise to the saying 'As sure as God's in Gloucestershire' and leaving a wealth of churches behind.

To the east of the county the limestone hills made good grazing and small villages became prosperous with the wool trade of the Middle Ages, whilst further south, the Stroud valleys expanded as the clothing industries of the eighteenth and nineteenth centuries produced some of the best cloth in England.

The buildings left behind by all these different people and the land that they altered and worked has made a very beautifuly and varied county which naturally splits into three distinctive areas – the Forest of Dean, the Vale and River Severn, and the Cotswold Hills. No one part is more lovely than the others, as each is so different and the whole county is rich in history and ancient monuments.

From the higher points the views of surrounding shires are magnificent whilst in the many hollows and folds are exquisite churches and some of the prettiest villages and market towns.

Gloucestershire is more than just the well-known Cotswolds, and there are many unspoilt and secret places to visit and enjoy without bumping into coach loads of people.

The **Forest of Dean** to the west of the county is one of its more mysterious parts. Isolated between the Wye and the Severn, not quite Welsh and yet barely part of Gloucestershire, the position of this Royal Forest has contributed to its feeling of isolation and the independent nature of its people. It is a strange mixture of beautiful woodland, slag heaps and scattered villages. Now that the mining has stopped and ferns and sheep have taken over, the industrial sites have become nostalgically attractive.

The ancient Britons and Celts first used the area to mine the ore and smelt and shape the iron – many of the mines being veins open to the surface known as 'scowles'. When the Romans came they traded with the locals and left mine workings, stretches of excellent highways, villas and temples, scattered across the whole forest. By the Middle Ages charcoal and iron ore were big business and this small patch of industry supplied the rest of England and much of Europe – the nearby estuary and river channel making export easy.

At Clearwell an old iron mine has recently been opened to the public. Ray Wright, a Forester, bought the old workings at a time when some of the old miners were still alive – so that during the excavations when old tools and objects were found in the blocked shafts he was able to hear first hand how and why these things were used. He now has a great knowledge of the old ways and at the head of the mine he made a collection of the pieces found. The engine room has been restored and some of the underground caverns are big enough to be used for barbecues and parties.

Forest timbers were used to make some of the great English warships and frigates that stormed up and down the seas of the world and kings came down from London to visit their royal hunting grounds – in those days full of boar and deer.

It is still a Royal Forest but now administered by the Forestry Commission, so slag heaps have been made into viewing points and tracks and trails pushed through the woodland thus opening up to the public a rather closed area.

The Forest of Dean has always been a strange secret place cut off from the rest of the county with broad dialects, customs and ancient privileges.

A man over twenty-one and born within the Hundred (or Parish) of St Briavels, the old capital of the forest, providing he has worked in a mine for a year and a day, is entitled to be granted a 'gale' or mining allotment from whence he can dig free coal.

Years ago these free-miners always used their rights and applied yearly for their gales, and although few people bother now, the centuries' old rights and disregard for authority are fiercely preserved.

At St Briavels the custom of throwing the Bread and Cheese Dole is still performed. It is connected with the rights to gather firewood which hardly anyone does, yet locals feel the tradition must be maintained.

It is a charming ceremony performed after evensong on Whit Sunday. At present, the Cresswick family are the 'throwers' (the men only) and one of them stands on the old pound wall to scatter the tiny cubes of bread and cheese into the gathered crowds. It is said that it will never go mouldy from one year to the next and to keep some by you brings good luck – the miners always carried some in their pockets.

The Verderers' Court meets at Speech House in the heart of the forest to deal with Commoners' rights

Font in the Parish Church of St Briavels, Forest of Dean.

and in the past malefactors had their hands cut off or swung from the gallows at St Briavels for violating their privileges. Speech House is now a hotel but the court still meets once a year.

A hundred and fifty years ago the area existed on mining only, and poor wages were supplemented by the free coal and running a few animals on the common land.

Agriculture and farming came second. A few cattle were kept for each family's butter and cheese and although sheep were numerous enough to warrant seasonal sheep sales at Little Dean and sheep dog trials at Cinderford, there were never any big market centres in the Forest. Surplus stock was taken to either Ross or Gloucester. When the railways came and opened up the area, farmers who could afford to send their beasts by rail did so, otherwise the long walk into the weekly markets made the animals a good deal less valuable at the end of the journey.

The withdrawal of the railways by Beeching's cuts in the 1960s has left the area strewn with skeleton platforms, old shunting buffers and miles of rusty overgrown track – an idyllic place for railway enthusiasts. The Dean Forest Railway Society at Norchard near Lydney has open steam days in the summer with all the nostalgic smells and noises that many people will remember with affection.

The Forest of Dean area has many unique remnants of its past. At Newland the big church is called 'Cathedral of the Forest' and one of the monuments inside is a brass showing a miner in medieval costume. In those days they worked by the light of candles stuck into a ball of clay which was wedged onto a stick; this stick was held between their teeth whilst they hacked at the coal seams. As if this was not bad enough, there are stories of rough lumps of iron ore being chucked down the shirts to irritate their backs and make them hasten to the surface with their loads. (Many of these things can be seen at the Clearwell Iron Mines). At Ruardean and Little Dean Church there are some of the most beautiful church memorials in the district. They fill the churchyards sometimes undisturbed and submerged by grass and ferns, and sometimes as part of tidying-up processes in ranks against the churchyard wall; but the pretty pink sandstone tablets and tombs are worth examining for their charming examples of symbolism and beliefs.

At Ruardean there are weeping willows, praying hands and baskets of fruit and at Little Dean a gravestone to a 'Verderor of Ye Forest' is festooned with cherubic heads and garlands of flowers.

You cannot travel far in the forest without coming across large boulders, outcrops and standing stones. Some are visible from the main roads and trips to the others take you through delightful parts of the woodland.

Thought by the more romantic to have been left by the Druids long before the Roman invasion, these monoliths and menhirs still incite arguments as to their origin.

Some think the Druids fashioned them for religious purposes when life was guided by spiritual beliefs and senses were acutely tuned to the earth. They were perhaps used as ceremonial tables and markers of the early forms of communication known as ley lines.

Perched on a hill near Staunton, the Buckstone is an enormous boulder that used to rock on a pivot. Believers say the the Druids used the oscillations as oracles or the reverberations as alarms; geologists say time and the elements produced this stone, but either way it has fascinated people for centuries. After many attempts to dislodge the Buckstone, six men from Monmouth toppled it in 1885. Now it sits embedded in concrete and no longer rocks. (The *Secret Forest* by Ray Wright is a good guide to all the stones and can be bought from the Coleford Bookshop.)

The towns of the Forest are scarred by hardship and some spoiled by modernization, but they lie in glorious and unspoilt countryside. Narrow roads wind

Standing stone at Staunton, Forest of Dean.

The White Hart (public House), Coleford, Forest of Dean.

up and down over the hills and through the woods; little red houses perch amongst the fir trees and in the valleys there are fruit farms and orchards.

The town of Coleford has had it centre ripped out and supermarkets and roundabouts replace town halls and market buildings. Around the church tower in the centre – what was the market place – you can find a few pretty porches and windows amongst the fairly nasty modern façades.

It was originally settled by Iron Age man working the nearby 'scowles' and the word 'Coleford' refers to a charcoal ford at a time when this ancient industry was important. On the outskirts are industrial archaeological sites – an eighteenth-century blast furnace at Whitecliff – and tram roads and old railways can be followed with care.

Mitcheldean's centre has been swamped by a copying manufacturer but the church and surrounding cottages have escaped. The Town Hall, a small square sandstone building tucked off the main road, is one of the few remaining market halls of the forest. Most people seemed to walk to Gloucester with any spare livestock and the rest were probably too busy in the mines to make much market business.

Cinderford is the only town with a market now as people continue to use Gloucester as a centre, but it is a well run 'Spook' market from the Moreton-in-Marsh company and appreciated by the isolated cottages and hamlets that catch the specially run buses on market days.

Micheldean Town Hall or Market House, a square sandstone building that has survived the recent changes of this little Forest town.

Newnham lies on the ede of the Forest proper and was its major town. Close by the River Severn a trading place and a port, it was near enough to the rest of Gloucestershire for fashions to permeate and give it a grander air then other Forest towns.

The main street is lined with all periods of architecture – pretty Georgian brick residences with wrought-iron balconies brought over from Cheltenham Spa; well-proportioned shop windows reach right down to street level and here and there are timber-framed buildings with narrow gables and slanting sash windows.

The river narrows and sweeps round into a great horseshoe bend at Newnham, making it a natural crossing place before bridges were built upstream at Gloucester. As far back as the first century AD the Romans made it their crossing point from the Bristol/ Gloucester road to Cardiff (and apparently travelling with mammoths as their bones have been found in the river mud!). Stone benches spanned the water until the shifting level of the bed of the Severn caused the early medieval settlers to use a ferry.

For centuries a passenger ferry operated continuously from Arlingham Passage on the other side until it ceased in the 1930s. In 1872 a single track railway opened, chugging across the river from Sharpness

carrying coal in and out of the Forest. The bridge, twenty-one spans supported on cylindrical piers, came to a sad end in 1960 when a tanker collided with it on a dark foggy night. It was never repaired, being little used, and eventually, demolished. Since 1966 a mighty suspension bridge carries the M4 across to Wales at Aust, and Gloucester is no longer the lowest bridging point of the Severn.

The regular ferry at Newnham saved a journey of **thirty miles** or so via Gloucester and made it a busy **crossing point**. Horses and carriages were taken over, **people crossed to go to work and children to attend school**. Farmers from Westbury and the Forest loaded feather light lambs onto it in spring to fatten **them** on the rich pastures at Arlingham and Oldbury **and** staggered back in the autumn, the fat sheep barely portable.

Today there is no ferry but the pub at Arlingham is still called The Passage.

Being near the Forest, Newham traded in coal and timber and the river was busy with traffic. If you walk along Church Road (the original main route through the town) you join Severn Street (formerly Passage Lane) where passengers would have climbed up from the ferries and cargoes stowed in the warehouses at the top. A flight of steps takes you the last bit into the 'new' High Street and opposite is Dean Road, an ancient hollow way that the Romans followed into the forest.

Newnham Church is at the top of the High Street rise on a cliff promontary and has been resited several times. The present one is Victorian although the churchyard is full of fascinating old memorials and headstones.

The back of the graveyard overlooks the river bend and in the summer the footpath is thick with pink and white valerian, and it is a lovely place to view the slow-moving Severn. Motorists who rush through the town seeing only the High Street miss a lot.

In the eighteenth century Newnham changed from the usual market town to a fashionable resort on the banks of the river. Elevated walks were made around the old castle mound and town improvements removed the Court House and Market Hall and put up elegant residences in place of medieval cottages. The river used to run right into the bottom of the High Street, and at high tide cargoes could be floated straight up to cellars and storehouses. Carriages had to splash through the water so a properly surfaced road was welcomed by travellers.

The main coaching inn then was the Victoria Hotel

and the faded grandeur of its columns and porch is supposed to be influenced by Frampton Court, a manor house across the river.

Today it is still the main hotel of the town – the interior darkly panelled, the bars cosy and welcoming. In the window halfway up the staircase is a most exquisite piece of stained glass. A small diamond pane decorated in sulphurous yellows and blues shows the grasshopper and the ants arguing in Aesop's fable. 'The grasshopper came unto the aunts, and demanded part of theer corne, whereupon they did

aske what hee had done in the sommer, and he saide he had sang and they saide if you sang in the sommer then daunce in the winter' – dated Anno 1622.

In the middle of the High Street the grassy 'chains' are really the old foundations of medieval shops and houses, and for many years have been planted with daffodils. In the spring people came miles to see the beautiful carpet of yellow flowers down the middle of this attractive riverside town.

Newnham is one of the best places to view the Severn and you can understand how important it was

Severn Street (the old road to the ferry), Newnham.

to people before motor transport. Along Dean Road and past the pound, a few cottages and farmhouses, the narrow road climbs up to a vantage point called 'Pleasant Stile'. From here the whole wide bend of the river is visible. In the Vale are the spires of Gloucester and Cheltenham and beyond the wooded ridges of Haresfield and Nibley and the high Wolds; to the west the widening estuary opens out into the Bristol Channel.

Between Frampton and Awre, the river narrows and this sudden change of width funnels big tides up into a racing wave known as the Bore. There is quite a big one each month but at certain times of the year (always advertised in the local press) the Bore is very spectacular, flooding the meadows and swamping the roads. The rise and fall of the river is large and in 1981 houses near the bank experienced water halfway up their groundfloor windows when the tide rose to the highest level since 1710.

Elmore Back and Stonebench are good places to view the Bore and at night from the Minsterworth road you are sufficiently high up to keep dry.

Waiting in the dark, listening hard for the rushing sound of the wave, is an eerie exciting experience; you seem to wait ages and then suddenly it curls fast around the bend, rises noisily past you, leaving restless lapping banks, washed and wet.

The part of the Severn that flows through Gloucestershire is both navigable and tidal and therefore anyone has the right to fish the river. This right however, after centuries of open fishing, now requires a licence from the River Authorities and does not extend to parts of the bank in private ownership.

There are public stretches at Gatcombe (where Drake is supposed to have stayed to choose Forest oaks for the English fleet) jealously guarded by locals where spirits run high and fishermen are not very polite to one another.

To catch the salmon, banks of 'putchers' or conical weirs stretch out from the banks, while in the shallows hand-held lave nets are used. In the deeper pools stop nets are suspended from boats. Fish is plentiful. There is fresh salmon to buy, and if you ask in the Westbury and Newnham public houses, you will be directed to farms with bulging cold stores.

Lampreys are still caught in the river, but no longer considered a delicacy; they are used as eel bait. It is elvers (baby eels) that are the much sought-after harvest from the river.

Between March and May these white, thread-like fish fry are scooped up on the tides and sold to the several elver stations along the river. More profitable alive than dead (five pounds a kilo at the right time in the season) they are kept moist in shallow trays and sent all over the world.

In Gloucestershire, eating a plate of elvers is known as a 'feed' and a good appetite can see the end to a pound at a time. They are either fried in bacon fat or cooked with an egg broken into them.

According to those who look after it, the river is not used enough commercially but at weekends children can be seen pottering about in the shallows netting flat fish, and sometimes in the summer at low tide there is a rhythmic thump of horses exercising on the sand banks.

Flat lanes meander backwards and forwards to the edge of the river between pasture land and orchards but the road to **Frampton** from the Passage is a straight Roman one. This village is well known for its long green and supposed associations with Rosamund, the romantic mistress of Henry II, and member of the Clifford family (who still live there as Lords of the Manor).

A high wall runs down the length of the green; pink, buff, blue and purple bricks made with clay dug from the river silt and having that beautiful variety of colours of things hand-made. Practically, they are rather poor quality as too much salt in the clay makes some cottage interiors pour with water in the wet weather, and Frampton is notorious for its damp river mists.

Around the village there is also the odd big black brick that has found its way over from the old glass factory at Newnham when there was a regular ferry.

Frampton has an amazing selection of architecture. Bordering onto the green are stone houses, thatched cottages and small brick mansions. In the garden of Frampton Court is the orangery in the Strawberry Hill Gothic style. Cruck cottages are close to an excellent modern house in The Street and near the church a fourteenth-century barn still has its sides filled in with traditional wattle.

The Gloucester and Sharpness canal runs between the village and the river and, being higher than the fields, it is very odd to see tankers apparently steaming through the fields. The bridge-keepers' houses along the canal are miniature Greek temples with life belts hanging between the Doric columns.

The Frampton Deer Roast in August (the Monday nearest the 15th) is all that remains of markets and

Bridge-keeper's house on the Berkeley-Sharpness canal near Frampton.

fairs in the village. Old traditions can easily disappear, so it is good to hear of new ones starting up. In 1966 a local coal merchant read of a Cambridge student disposing of a large number of sausages and boasted to the village butcher that he could do better. A contest was held on the green and farmer Les Koole won, eating three pounds of sausages in eight or nine minutes.

From that time it became an annual Easter Monday event and as elvers, the local speciality, are in season then, they were added to the eating contest in 1969.

Now hoards of people from miles around come to watch the gastronomic excesses of eight contestants who sit down to a pound of sausages or a plate of white stringy elvers with their black beady eyes, cooked that morning over an open fire.

Near the Gloucestershire, Hereford and Worcester border the River Avon joins the Severn; salt ways and Roman roads are old routes now overtaken by main roads and motorways. In this well-watered flat land between the Malverns and Bredon Hill is the town of Tewkesbury, surrounded by ancient farms and religious houses.

At Deerhurst, a few miles to the south, you will find both; the timbered Priory Farm sits right up against the church which is small and charming, full of scrolled capitals and little Norman faces peering down on the pews.

Down the lane, Odda's Chapel is even older and named after one of Tewkesbury's Saxon founders.

Bare and narrow, it is very characteristic of the early chapels that survived the Dark Ages, being also the largest Saxon church in England. Travelling on to **Tewkesbury**, first glimpses of the square Norman tower of the abbey show you the extent of building skills that developed in a few hundred years.

The town built up around the Benedictine monastery that started in the eighth century. Rather run down by the tenth century, it had a glorious second coming with all the new buildings (including the tower) of the 1100s and 1200s.

Inside the Abbey, magnificent round Norman pillars support the nave and for ten pence in a slot, a set of lights illuminate the splendid sea of green, red and gold roof bosses. Known as 'lierne' vaulting, and put up in 1330, the bosses over the interceptions illustrate the life of Christ, the Evangelists, and angels playing bagpipes and peculiar instruments.

Tewkesbury growing under the folds of the abbey developed as a market town and the River Severn, running parallel to the main street, provided a swifter, cleaner form of transport than the muddy roads.

Apart from a slight attempt to turn it into a Regency spa, Tewkesbury has remained unchanged since the Middle Ages. The Industrial Revolution passed it by and over enthusiastic Victorian restorers were put off by William Morris. His fierce letters to proposed 'good works' by Gilbert Scott resulted in the setting up of the Society for the Protection of Ancient Buildings in 1877.

Decaying buildings were rescued and since then

Capital in Saxon church, Deerhurst.

sensitive repairs and generous benefactors have helped preserve a very complete example of a medieval town.

In Church Street a whole row of merchants' shops escaped the 60s rebuilding blitz and have been restored to their natural soft grey and white appearance. One shop is always open to the public and displays how very simply homes and shops were furnished. As the market grew up in this area around the Abbey gates, these shops were probably some of the first permanent ones to be built. Elizabeth I granted a Wednesday market and a little Spook market is still held on this day near Trinity Church at the back of the High Street.

At the beginning of September the entire length of Barton Street is filled with chairoplanes, big wheels and open booths when the traditional mop fair is celebrated with a modern pleasure fair. It is very peculiar to see the narrow road with its timbered buildings, crammed with the arms and legs of vast modern machinery, but there is a bona-fide Gypsy Rose Lee in attendance to tell your fortune and bring you luck.

Tewkesbury has always been a milling town and the mill of 'John Halifax Gentlemen' at the edge of the river is now a restaurant. Literary connections are many and the John Moores Museum recently opened in Church Street. His love of nature links the museum with the Mythe Nature Reserve just north of the town. Near an old salt route, disused rail tracks and clay pits form a protected area where woad (strangely having yellow flowers) grows wild and nightingales are heard in early summer. A little book in the museum lists the vast number of butterflies and plants that can be seen.

Tewkesbury's old streets are threaded with narrow alleys giving short cuts to parallel streets or access to cottages and yards. Opposite the Abbey entrance is one called Old Baptist Chapel Court, the chapel in the alley having been bought by Tewkesbury Borough in the 1970s and restored.

It is one of the oldest Baptist buildings, starting life as a fifteenth-century house with open hall and galleries. As the movement gained strength it was converted into a public place of worship, a minister's room added in 1720 and the galleries extended around three sides. Now it is a small panelled building, very simple and uncluttered, in an attractive setting. The Victorian cottages next door adjoin the burial ground where many elders and ministers and Baptists families are buried.

On the outskirts of Tewkesbury towards Gloucester, the fields and meadows around Gupshill Manor mark the last battle of the Wars of the Roses fought in 1471, and now known as the Bloody Meadow. Apart from this period of English strife and on a more homely note, Tewkesbury is famous for its mustard. Housewives – using old cannon balls – pounded the mustard seed with horseradish root to make a distinct and rather sharp paste. It can still be bought in the town and many pubs serve it with their hamburgers and hotdogs.

Winchcombe is tucked in a valley at the edge of the high wolds and is typical of the stone towns of this sheep country. The biggest farmers, the wealthiest and often the best, were the monasteries and the abbey at Winchcombe was rich in Edward III's reign with revenue from the sheep they ran on the hills.

The complex of buildings that used to stand next to the Parish Church (nothing remains now except foundations in a private garden) became the mainstay of the town, and although there was often bad feeling and animosity from the locals, it had turned the town into a prosperous market centre by the Middle Ages.

The market did not sell wool only. English and foreign merchants visited Winchcombe to buy cloth, coal, wine and fish as well as exotic spices, figs and raisins.

In amongst the present shops in Gloucester Street and High Street are fine big houses left by the wealthy and pretty rows of almshouses donated by benefactors.

Like so many of these Cotswold towns the church is glorious. Ralph Boteler, first Baron Sudeley, having rebuilt the castle, poured money into rebuilding the church, and because so much was done at one time, the wide nave is mostly a delicate perpendicular style.

Yarnell's Alley, Tewkesbury.

Along the aisles are relics of Winchcombe's past — stone coffins that are supposed to belong to the legendry St Kenelm and King Kenulf whose deaths made the town a place of pilgrimage; an altar cloth made from a priest's cope with a border embroidered by Catherine of Aragon when she stayed at Sudeley; and a big dark wooden almsbox that could be opened only when the vicar and both churchwardens were present.

The outside of the church is decorated with wonderful gargoyles — men and beasts with pop eyes and screaming mouths. One looks just like the Madhatter from *Alice in Wonderland* and the moustachioed Knight with the toothy grin is supposed to be Sir Ralph.

Sudeley is barely a mile from the town, down an avenue of beech trees and through green parkland. With its splendid history of kings and queens it is difficult to imagine it had lapsed to a mere alehouse in the nineteenth century.

Since then successive owners have restored the gardens and filled the building with sumptuous furniture and pictures. Travelling exhibitions often fill the corridors and halls and the Cheltenham Music Festival stages concerts and entertainments in the big courtyard.

Whilst royalty stayed in the lovely surroundings at Sudeley, the merchants of Winchcombe also found their share of wealth in their sheep and wool.

One particular woolman, who started in Winchcombe but actually made his fortune in Berkshire, has a book written about him. It gives a very vivid picture of the busy industry that thrived in the wool counties of England in the sixteenth century; 'the warehouses some being filled with wool, some with flock, some with Woad and Madder, and some with broadcloth and kersies ready dyed and dressed, beside great numbers of others, some stretched on tenders, some hanging on poles and a great many more lying wet in other places'. (Deloney's *Pleasant and Delightful Life of Jack of Newbury*, 1596.)

After the Dissolution many towns floundered and Wincombe had a weekly market granted in an attempt to improve trade. Locals tried tobacco growing and tradition has it that Sir Walter Raleigh lived at nearby Brockhampton, planting the first tobacco in the town (the spot is marked by new houses in Tobacco Close).

Winchcombe subsided into a sleepy market town, considerably quieter and less important than it had been in the days of the Abbey, until Victorian enthusiasm replaced the delapidated Town Hall with

Gargoyle on the Parish Church, Winchcombe.

the present arcaded building, and revived fairs and commerce.

Mop fairs were held in market towns and farmers and householders would attend to choose new servants. In Winchcombe it took place in October and those looking for employment lined the market place showing something of their trade – shepherds held crooks or wore wool in their hats, carters stood with whipcords and domestic servants with brooms or mops.

When the bargaining was over, a shilling was given to the servant which bound them for a year (although most towns held Runaway Mops a week later and those not happy with their new employers could try for another position).

North Street was Horsefair Street then, and twice a year was crammed with Irish and Welsh ponies and horses tied shoulder to shoulder, and teams of horses pulling freshly painted wagons paraded the main streets on fair day.

In the nineteenth century, a small sum bought a licence to sell beer on fair and market days and a bush (the ancient alehouse sign) was hung outside.

Modern Winchcombe is lively and the shops small and quaint. Most of the old fronts have been kept and many shopkeepers have pretty windows in which to display goods.

In North Street the baker's window is always beautifully arranged and well known locally for its frequently changing display. The baker's wife (by coincidence their family name is North) makes the display topical or seasonal. Sometimes there is a basket full of different breads – plaits, sticks, granaries and split tops; sometimes a pile of small breadrolls, curls and scrolls like Saxon carvings, and other times mice and hedgehogs made of bread.

Mr North, a third generation baker whose brothers are all in the trade, has discovered that his shop has been a bakehouse for hundreds of years, the side alley much scarred by the wheels of bread-loaded handcarts. *Reminiscences of Winchcombe* by John Oakley tells of Whitsuntide games played with penny loaves dipped in treacle, no doubt baked in North Street. This little book confirms the notion that Whitsuntide was a popular time for merrymaking, heralding the coming summer and anticipating abundant crops.

The awful game Kickshins, peculiar to the Cotswold district, was apparently very popular and Wincombe men proud of their hardy reputation.

Today the fairs and mops have gone, but much of the hilarity is retained at the 'Dover's Hill Olympic Games' held on the hills above the town.

In the second half of the nineteenth century, in direct opposition to the Victorian Industrial Age, artists and poets all over England created a new romantic era. William Morris steered the Arts and Crafts Movement along a precarious route of hand-made crafts competing with mass-produced articles.

As part of the 'back to the land' philosophy, Morris moved to the edge of Oxfordshire; his influence was felt nationally, and is very evident in Gloucestershire and the Cotswolds. In an enthusiastic and ambitious attempt to put into practice those new ideals, Charles Ashbee, architect and designer, moved his Guild of Handicrafts from Whitechapel to the rural but faded market town of **Chipping Campden**.

Once an important wool centre built up by local merchants, Chipping Campden kept going through the wool decline by turning to silk and flax. By the time the London Guild arrived the neglected butter market and dusty streets were exactly the 'unspoilt' environment they desired.

Today there are many beautiful buildings for the visitor to admire and it is probably due to the Guild's interest and benefactors like artist F.L. Griggs, that so much of the town is preserved.

When Ashbee arrived in Campden in 1901, he lived in Woolstaplers Hall. He then took over a disused silk mill and eventually employed over seventy men and boys in craftwork. They did cabinet making, wrought-iron work, copper and silver work as well as attracting other artists and craftsmen to the area.

Unfortunately politics, mis-management and places like Liberty's of London producing well-designed goods at competitive prices, forced the Guild to disband after seven years, but their influence is lasting. All over the Cotswolds there are church windows, memorials, houses and pieces of furniture in their style and the Silk Mill is still the home of designers and craftsmen. On the first floor descendants of George Hart, Ashbee's last Guildsman, continue to work in silver.

Campden is no longer a market town (although there are accounts of vast yearly fleece sales right up to the Second World War), it thrives now as a tourist centre, busy throughout the year.

Above the town, through leafy lanes and hedgerows with wonderful views of the Vale of Evesham, is Dover Hill. On the eve of Spring Bank Holiday this is the site of the 'Cotswold Olympics' – a night of games and entertainment that finishes with a wake and a carnival the next day.

The history and origin of the games is very interesting. Robert Dover (his family came from Norfolk) was an educated legal man, and he settled in the area in the early years of the seventeenth century.

In a climate of Renaissance thinking and Shakespeare's new plays this barrister started to organize yearly games – some say merely reorganize existing Cotswold Whitsuntide revelries – to accommodate all types from the nobility to the lower classes.

Historians believe these games, that are older than the better known Highland Games, were established by permission of James I, and patrons travelled miles to take part in what was considered an attempt to emulate the games of classical Olympia long since lapsed.

Described as 'jovial, generous and mirth-making', the Games included much running, jumping and leaping as well as throwing contests. Prizes were yellow flags and favours and silver castles, and

'Rustic' porches on old cottages at Brockhampton, a village between Cheltenham and the high Stow road.

studded dog collars were given for horse-racing and coursing. From accounts it is evident that the scale and importance of the games were unsurpassed by anything in the seventeenth century.

After years of success this hilltop spectacle was closed for a while by the Puritans, who also banned other festivals with pagan origin, thus killing numerous English traditions.

Many were not revived but the popularity of the 'Olimpick Games' was remembered after the Restoration and it started again with renewed vigour.

There are wonderful accounts of the dancing and racing contests in long verses by contemporary poets. There were ladies' races with smocks as prizes, shoes to be won by good jig dancing and a silver spoon to be won by grinning through a horse collar.

The Games gained a fresh surge in the nineteenth century and evoked tremendous rivalry between neighbouring villages. Shinkicking was again most renowned with men hardening up their shins by beating them with planks and hammers (the contest is between two men who hold each other's shoulders and with steel-capped boots kick the lower leg of the opponent).

Morris dancing – more genteel – was equally popular and it is due to the Games continuing so long unabated, that the Bampton Morris Men over the border in Oxfordshire still survive in such a pure state.

Unfortunately the growing industrial influence of visiting crowds from the Midlands turned the Games into a rowdy pandemonium for days on end, with thefts, drunkeness and stalls and games spoilt. Heavy support from the Church caused the Olimpicks to be closed down in 1887.

The Procession and Wake continued and managed to survive the two world wars. The Games were revived once in 1951 as part of the Festival of Britain celebrations, but this time the infamous shinkicking was only a display, not a contest.

In the early 60s there were plans to start the Games

Pilgrims' bath and gallery, George Inn, Winchcombe.

again and in 1966 they were re-established on the hill in a form of revelry to accommodate modern crowds and requirements.

Now each year there are tugs of war and marathons, bands play and people crowd in to see exhibitions of the old sports. A bonfire and firework display end the evening and everyone joins in the torchlight procession down the hill into Campden.

The Cotswolds are famous for their limestone buildings and up until the last fifty years every man born on the Cotswolds could use stone. Building or carving, how to shape and pare the limestone so that it not only lasted for hundreds of years but enhanced the landscape – was an instinct they were born with. With the interest in old skills and desire for conservation, stonework is better respected than it was in the 50s and 60s and as one travels around the area one can find many masons and wallers at work.

'One a-top o'two, and two a-top o'one' is the old adage, but it is not as simple as that and the eye of a good waller is so practised that he rarely picks up a stone twice.

Above Wincombe near Stanway is one of the larger stone quarries still being worked. It is like a monumental amphitheatre with enormous orange blocks and great heaps of rubble littering the excavated area, like giant props on a stage. In the past, the Cotswolds had quarries around every bend and farmers and estates had small workings of their own that supplied enough stone to build and repair their walls and farm buildings. The colour and texture of the limestone varies enormously and an experienced mason can site the origin of a building block just by looking at it.

All the great buildings of the area are fashioned from local stone and despite the horrid reconstituted sham stuff now being made, those quarries still operating have to work hard to keep up with the demand for dressed stone.

Along the valley of the Windrush there are stonemasons cutting and tapping with aged ebony tools. At Farmington in tumbledown sheds warmed by old-fashioned stoves, they work at benches covered with bits of carpets using tools made by George Swinford. Here the stone comes out yellow and dries to almost white and makes fine building material and fireplaces. Recently, excavations have exposed four hundred year old shafts left from the times when the stone was mined not quarried and it took laden ox-carts six weeks to reach London.

Visit practically any church on either side of the

Capital and wall decorations in Hampnett Church.

Stow road to see exquisitely carved pieces of local stone worked by local men who knew how to get the best from it.

Moreton-in-Marsh is on the Roman Fosse Way that runs straight as a die from Cirencester up into Leicestershire. It used to be called Moreton Henmersche until it became better known as a fording place of the Evenlode. Close to Vale and Wold the wool and weaving trade profited, and driving through it today Moreton is unmistakably a market town. The extremely wide street and turreted Redesdale Hall is quite swamped by stalls on market day – the pubs and cafés full of people resting and in the summer the greens are covered with weary shoppers.

The market is the biggest in the Cotswolds, very much the size of those in the Midlands and the north. Coaches and buses flood into the big car park and the town doubles in population once a week. People saunter across the roads, children and dogs trail behind grown-ups who push in and out of the narrow corridors between the trestles. Stall-holders shout their wares and the travelling butchers will accept cheques, but not Embassy coupons, to the amusement of the waiting public.

The three hundred or so stalls are organized by Spook Enterprises, the biggest private market operators in Great Britain, who boast that they are responsible for the largest markets in the world outside Addis Ababa. Their offices are in Moreton and it is not surprising that the market is so large, being the home town of the owner Nigel Maby.

He decided some years ago that he could do better than the one stall on Evesham fruit market and gradually through business-like organization took over the running of existing markets, bought charters and started new ones. Now his company runs thirty-five markets that have built up good reputations with both traders and punters. Special coaches do round trips to outlying places and all the stalls trade from 8.30 a.m. until 4.30 p.m.

Spook markets are easily recognized by the strange pregnant ghost on pennant-shaped flags. Being rather pale at school, Nigel Maby was nicknamed 'Spook' and he liked the image of markets appearing and disappearing overnight – the pregnancy denotes expansion. The logo is odd but the markets are good, and the business young and enthusiastic.

The Fosse Way runs on to **Stow-on-the-Wold** (in parts old Roman foundations can be found beneath grassy verges), another market town founded on the commercial possibilities of its road junctions.

The Town House and Cross House concerned with market operations have gone but the cross, worn smooth with use, remains intact. A fine circle of buildings surround the green where the stocks are, and all the banks and shops are in beautiful houses. St Edwards Café has particularly elegant fluted pilasters on its market façade.

In the narrow streets of the rest of the town, humbler cottages step straight onto the pavement and the tiny long alleys off Sheep Street are supposed to have been used to count sheep when the town was a wool centre. But they may just be the access to the jumble of small houses and gardens behind the shop fronts.

In the summer, the church tower is open to visitors and it is a very long, narrow steep climb up past the ticking clock and the heavy bells to the top. From between the stone parapets you can easily see Moreton and Chipping Norton and if it is not misty,

over to the flatter lands of Warwickshire. Looking below one realizes how big the market square is and it is interesting to see the town spread out like a three-dimensional map.

Four times a year – March, May, July and October – the fields over the Fosse swarm with people and animals for Stow Fair. In Cotswold country, fairs of the Middle Ages became dominated by sheep, but kept going through wars and changes in trade, by becoming pleasure fairs or dealing in horses.

Now these quarterly gatherings are some of the most popular horse fairs in the country, attracting people from all over Great Britain and Ireland. The auctioneers' reputation for good animals and fair dealing, along with Stow being right in the heart of excellent horse country, has made the fairs expand at a time when others are petering out.

The best ones to visit are the charter ones of May and October, the autumn being a particularly pretty time of the year in that part of the country.

Auctioning starts smartly at ten in the morning and goes on until four with two main rings, one selling harness and the other, horses. In adjoining fields the lots include farm machinery and wagons.

On an autumn morning the distant fields are bright and sparkling with long winterish shadows over the furrows and, around the windy sale rings, people, children and animals mill about as the whole spectrum of English country life turns out to see what is for sale. The horses vary from minute furry Shetlands to cobs and hunters, and there are a lot of genuine bargains to be had.

In May and October the gypsies come, adding their own special colour and characteristics to the day, as well as their own way of buying and selling.

On charter days anyone is allowed to pitch on the roadside and the chaos of the fields is swelled by the stalls and horse boxes lined up on the verges.

Originally the travellers came only for the horse dealing, running out their horses along the Fosse, but now they sell brass and harness and other odds and ends.

There are always a few barrel-topped caravans camped at the roadside. You don't see these traditional vehicles much anymore, but at Stow those that attend are beautifully decorated and the families' overflow is housed in square green tents with stove-pipes poking through the canvas.

They are complete units with chickens and goats, arriving a few days before the fair. Some have been attending these fairs for years and obviously use them

View from Stow-on-the-Wold church tower – which visitors can climb in the summer months.

as a time to meet with friends and relatives and catch up with news. These people are so handsome with their dark skins and jet black curls, the young girls grabbing the chance to show themselves off, parade about in twos, smiling and dressed in bright flashy clothes. At the end of the fair day, the business done and the wads of notes changed hands, the caravans are packed and gone before the auctioneers have finished cashing up.

Watching them, one gets an insight into how important markets and fairs were to country folk as days of merry-making and relief from the hard times the rest of the year.

The May and October sale days are followed by pleasure fairs in the town, and the fair folk look like urbanized gypsies. Wearing high-heeled boots and tan fur coats they come down from their machines and booths and mix with the other travelling people at the fair.

It is a day out for everyone and apart from the fast selling around the auction rings, the gypsies are busy selling off little Welsh yearlings from pens against the stone walls at the roadside. The shouting, pushing, coaxing, throng of people and animals makes a marvellous atmosphere.

Lechlade's nearness to the navigable Thames made it an early market town. St John's Bridge has long been a crossing point and in the late seventeenth century a well-known cheese fair was held there. Hundreds of wagons arrived loaded with farmhouse cheeses from Gloucestershire and north Wiltshire, and wharfs and warehouses were built to accommodate the trade.

Until the railways came, the river was used to move coal from the Forest of Dean. Today pleasure boats and rowing skulls are moored end to end and the banks are lined with fishermen. Green footpaths and causeways hung over with willows and hawthorn intersect low-lying fields, linking the town to the old toll bridges and the path to the church across these water meadows is a particularly pretty approach to the town.

Over Halfpenny Bridge a boat trip or a short drive takes you to the hamlet of Inglesham where a lovely Saxon church, a favourite with William Morris, is in need of care and attention. The nave is full of old damp box pews and the oak gate is sadly lop-sided.

Stage coach traffic brought people and business to Lechlade and a coaching inn in the square has a big archway and courtyard to accommodate the frequent carriages. Numerous little square gazeboes are dotted round the streets, used as private waiting rooms for ladies and gentlemen looking out for their transport.

There is in fact quite an eighteenth-century elegance to the whole town and behind some of the high walls are formal gardens and beautiful homes. Local builders offered ornate fashionable dwellings and Shelley strolling in the churchyard was inspired to write verse.

Lechlade was too close to Fairford for both to thrive as market towns although Lechlade managed to keep its livestock fair until the late 1950s. Remnants of the horsefair can be seen in Burford Street, where there are iron rings in the wall and the bookshop opposite sells very good prints of old market day photographs.

Gypsy caravans and tents at Stow Horse Fair.

Typically the church is in the corner of the market square, and there is an incredible collection of grotesque gargoyles leering down into the square from the sides of the church. There is no market now but the town's side roads are worth exploring.

Off the Burford Road out of the town is the village of **Filkins** which has a unique museum in a couple of simple cottages next to the village lock-up. These rooms are crammed with country bygones and owned by Mr George Swinford – a wonderful old man in his nineties with a memory as sharp as yesterday.

Coming from a Cotswold family, a stonemason by trade like his father and grandfather before him, he is an immense source of knowledge and country ways. He worked all his life in and around the village and at one time Sir Stafford Cripps, the politician, employed him to build extensions to the family home (now burnt down). Whilst excavating an old moat, Mr Swinford dug up the skeleton of a donkey and a donkey's shoe. He nailed the shoe up in his office and this was the beginning of his collection. With his lively and enquiring mind, he picked up and collected all sorts of objects during his work and as people heard of his interest, they brought him old bits from their sheds and attics.

Sir Stafford encouraged his collection and gave him two tumbledown single roomed cottages which Mr Swinford re-roofed and restored. Now the white-washed walls are hung with hundreds of objects and the tables and cupboards loaded with artifacts dating back to Roman times.

One room houses objects found in kitchens and living rooms and some are surprisingly sophisticated. A clockwork cooking jack still ticks round to turn the meat regularly and evenly whilst the cook deals with another task; an L-shaped piece of tin with a handle, called a 'Dutch oven', is lined with hooks so that it can be held in front of the open fire. Bacon stuck onto the hooks basted the bread in the tray below to produce a complete breakfast. Ordinary people with little extra money were practical and inventive and nothing was wasted. Mr Swinford has a good collection of bone tools – apple scoops and weaving needles, the making and carving probably done in the evenings by the light of coarse tallow candles which are also exhibited.

Gazebo in Lechlade.

There is a coffee grinder that belonged to William Morris as well as his old iron field easel, whilst next door are the larger objects and farm implements.

A craftsman himself, Mr Swinford handles them all with affection and respect. He knows exactly what each tool will do and as he picks them up unconsciously makes the correct movement, showing his understanding and skill. Amongst swede cutters and breast ploughs is a nineteenth century briar cutter. Recently Mr Swinford dug up a Roman one

The village lock-up, Filkins.

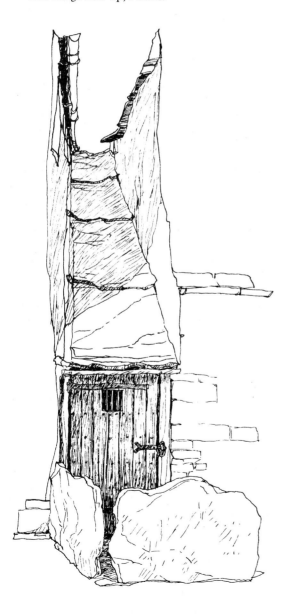

which is identical in design to the one his grandfather used.

Over the lintel hangs an object which is a great favourite with this old man, whose sense of fun got him into many scrapes at school and still manages to trick unwary visitors before they leave. The circular object is in fact a highwayman's horse shoe, its shape giving no clue as to the traveller's direction.

Around Filkins village many of the cottage gardens are fenced with great slabs of limestone which are peculiar to the area and come from the quarry up the road. Apparently worked by Napoleonic prisoners of war, thousands of roof tiles were dug by Mr Swinford and others before it closed in 1946.

The stone of this area splits itself into planks or 'presents' as they are locally called. They are easily quarried, needing only to have the edges dressed and holes pecked to make excellent roof tiles.

In 1981, the quarries were opened again by George Swinford's nephew and there is still plenty of stone waiting to be excavated.

People in the Cotswold region are now more conscious of natural building and conservation, so authentic materials are again in demand and the new quarrymen were experimenting with diamond-edged saws to quicken the pace, using Mr Swinford's old tools to finish them off.

Northleach sits on the Fosse between Stow and Cirencester and on the main Cheltenham to London road. The market square is now full of parked cars. The big wool church (sometimes with sheep grazing in the graveyard) has beautiful brasses and the lanes away from the noise and bustle of the through route are pretty and unspoilt.

At the cross roads the old prison has now opened as a country museum and apart from wagons and seasonal tools the original cells have been made into very authentic exhibits, as eerie recordings start automatically when the visitor steps over the threshold.

These 'Houses of Correction' were instigated by an influential man from Rodborough near Stroud, bearing the singularly peculiar name of Sir George Onesiphorous Paul.

This dedicated man led penal reform in Britain in the latter part of the eighteenth century and the building at Northleach was one of four new Houses of Correction to be put up in the county.

Designed by a leading prison architect, the cells (one for each man) radiated out around exercise yards

The large porch of Northleach church, one of the most celebrated of the Cotswold wool churches.

and the Keeper's Room. The night cells opened onto a balcony and the day cells onto the yard.

There were workshops and infirmaries and the square grey block to the right of the museum's entrance was the women's prison.

When Paul died, life became harder for the prisoners and there are photographs of men in treadwheels, a regular part of their daily routine. By the middle of the nineteenth century the climate had changed again and child labour and public hanging were abolished.

The prison became in turn a police station and a Petty Sessional Courthouse and in the 1930s a tramp station, before it was turned into a museum in 1981.

With expansion being an accepted part of present day life, **Cirencester** is one of those towns that has become smaller and less important than it was centuries ago.

When Britain was invaded in AD 43 victorious Roman armies flooded through the West Country and the Fosse Way was constructed to link Devon with Lincoln.

Cirencester was a place where patrolling troops were stationed. When the frontier moved forward a city was founded and it became the chief administrative town for the area. Known then as Corinium Dobunnorum, it had all the elegance and sophistication that a Roman citizen desired. As such a prosperous and imposing city it ranked second only to London.

Built to the usual efficient town grid system, the Fosse Way ran straight into the big forum. The parallel streets were lined with temples, public buildings and the houses lavishly furnished and decorated with mosaic floors.

The forum in the centre was the main market area (and Cirencester is one of the few towns in the West Country where market history can be traced back to the first century) paved with clean flagstones and surrounded by rows of colonnaded shops. Our modern shopping centres are hardly innovative.

A very credible picture of Roman Cirencester has been made in the Corinium Museum in Park Street. One can clearly imagine the town before the Dark Ages and subsequent rebuilding of the medieval period.

There is a big collection of altars and inscriptions and several large mosaics have been removed from their original sites. Convincing tableaux show shops, kitchens (with lavish menues – oysters, snails, stuffed dormice and peacocks) and brightly painted living rooms. A display of soldiers' equipment and armour belong to the Ermine Street Guard – a local society of enthusiasts who reconstruct the paraphernalia of the Roman Imperial Army. The stone-throwing machine and giant crossbar are both working life-size models.

One of the most intriguing exhibits is a palindrome or word square. It was found in 1868 scratched on a piece of wall plaster and is a square of five words:

R O T A S
O P E R A
T E N E T
A R E P O
S A T O R

It reads the same across, down, and back to front.

Experts cannot agree about its meaning but generally think it was a secret Christian sign. In translation it can be read as 'The great sower (i.e. God) holds in his hands all works; all works the great sower holds in his hands'; or visually the word TENET twice, forms a cross – but there are many other interpretations and the Museum publishes a very interesting little leaflet.

Roman rule came to an end in the fifth century and during the Dark Ages many of Corinium's buildings disappeared stone by stone into surrounding homesteads.

The road system helped the town to survive and it entered a new period of prosperity with the building of an abbey at the edge of the old Roman city.

Medieval planners ignored any existing street plan and wiggley streets shoot out at all angles from the market place. Trade increased rapidly under abbey control and the town became the most important wool market in the south Cotswolds.

The great Parish Church dominates the town with its cathedral-like frontage and sumptuous three-storeyed porch. In the delicate soaring style of the fifteenth century the abbot built the porch to contain business offices. After the Dissolution it was used as a Town Hall, and it has sheltered shoppers and market people for generations.

The area to the side where the crosses are is neatly paved and, in the sunshine of winter or summer, the whole building looks magnificent. It is obvious from the outside and the inside that massive alterations have gone on and there was much rebuilding in the medieval period. Huge clerestory windows flood the aisles with golden light and above the wall paintings and numerous memorials a wooden roof covers the delicate Tudor nave. The whole is pierced and hung with fine columns, arcades and pinnacles and gives an impression of weightlessness.

On Mondays and Fridays the wide market place is full of stalls with red and blue striped awnings, a contrast to the old limestone buildings and yet more colour alongside the washed ones; on Tuesdays sheep and cattle are auctioned off from the small cattle market near the Bathurst Estate.

Following the medieval tradition, the town has been a trading centre for many farming villages and older inhabitants remember being squashed with brothers and sisters into dog-carts to be driven the ten miles

The Market at Cirencester.

Cirencester market. Prospective buyers viewing the sheep at the weekly stock market.

into Cirencester. In his pocket the father carried samples of grain to tempt the merchants in the Corn Hall.

As a country town still, it has a good number of family businesses – saddlers, seed merchants and butchers. In Blackjack Street the pork butcher has a wonderful shop front with painted glass, animal heads and shiny coloured tiles.

Away from the centre, the streets are narrow enough to discourage much traffic and from the abbey grounds you can walk through Gloucester Street and Thomas Street past a variety of architecture. Amongst the humble cottages are clothiers' houses with Italianate façades and big hidden courtyards. Narrow alleys lead to tiny flourishing back gardens.

Until the nineteenth century Cecily Hill was the main road to Bisley and Stroud but now it leads into Cirencester Park, home of the Earl of Bathurst.

The first Earl of Bathurst, created in 1772, built the house, the park and livened up the town. In a period of gentle times he created with his friend Alexander Pope radiating rides and avenues that stretch all the way to Sapperton. At intervals thoughtfully provided follies and summerhouses made shelters for a little musing and no doubt a little dalliance.

Modern Cirencester has provided the people with excellent art and craft workshops. In Cricklade Street an old brewery has been turned into an arts centre with gallery, studios, a restaurant and a bakery. Resident artists include weavers, silversmiths, potters and basket weavers, to be seen at work on most days.

Craftsmanship is high in Gloucestershire and this may be a coincidence or a direct legacy from the Arts and Crafts Movement of the last century.

At one time Ernest Gimson and the Barnsley brothers, who were influenced by William Morris, settled in the area around Cirencester. They had various temporary accommodation in Bathurst Estate Mansions until 1900. Then they built themselves cottages at Sapperton with money earned from their furniture making and architecture. They had restored Daneway House whilst leasing it and kept it on as workshops and showrooms.

In 1981 the Dennys who occupy this beautiful house arranged an exhibition of Gimson and the Barnsley brothers' work and it was exciting to see pieces of furniture back in the place where they had been made.

Before the Gimson and Barnsley restorations the house had been in a sad condition, having been neglected by the family of yeoman sheep farmers who owned it since 1397.

In the bedrooms the ceilings are decorated with naively fashioned tulips in plasterwork, and in the sitting room strings of heavy cart horses plod across doorways.

There is much lettering all over the house, on windows, near doorways and on barn walls added by various tenants and visitors. In the living room a window is painted with a list of those who have lived there since the Hancox.

During the exhibition, rooms were filled with settles, circular tables and rush seated ladder-back chairs. The smallest piece was a dark oak child's chair, with a back supported by painted wooden characters from Sapperton village – a shepherd, a woodman, a wheelwright and two old ladies.

The Daneway men made their furniture in a locally obtained oak. Its method of construction – the dovetailing, pegging and wedging – were not disguised but treated as decoration and features made of them. The handles and fittings along with the honesty and simplicity of the whole piece of furniture characterizes their work, as do the chamfered edges.

Not always well-liked by critics, the Barnsley brothers and Gimson have nevertheless influenced Europe, the Bauhaus and ultimately our modern furniture.

Coming down off the high wolds, the **Stroud area** is the tail end of the Cotswolds and not so well known as the parts around Stow and Bourton.

The large fields and undulating open vistas are gone but instead deep-folded valleys hide tiny hamlets and houses cling to steep hillsides; in the bottom the waters of the River Frome have turned mill wheels for centuries, and when England's trade shifted from exporting wool to producing actual cloth, medieval merchants and Huguenots found excellent water supplies in the rivers and streams of the Stroud valleys.

Between the seventeenth and early nineteenth centuries, Dursley, Wotton-under-Edge, Painswick and Stroud flourished and grew rich from the famous west of England broadcloth.

Along the narrow valley from Stroud to Brimscombe, the developers packed a railway, a canal and a new road. Prior to this travellers had climbed from Cirencester through Bisley and into Stroud.

The coach traffic of the eighteenth century demanded a less tortuous route and another road was made up to Minchinhampton, over the Common and down through Butterow. Eventually, as clothiers and carriers complained bitterly of the four-mile journey to the mills at Chalford taking their loaded wagons a whole day, a new road – now the main A419 – was opened in 1815.

Whilst roads were gradually improved, the building of the Stroudwater Canal linking the Bristol Channel with the Thames and Severn also helped the growing industries around Stroud. Market towns like Cirencester and Lechlade were linked to a network of waterways that practically went east to west across this southern part of England. Unfortunately the canals (privately owned) were different widths, and a large inland port was built at Brimscombe to enable cargoes to be shifted to different sized narrow boats.

At Sapperton a long tunnel was driven through to Coates and bargees using it had to leave their horses and 'leg' their boats through lying on their backs, 'walking' along the roof of the tunnel, a slow and uncomfortable journey of two and a quater miles. The tunnel entrance at Coates has been restored and much of the canal towpaths can be walked; quiet unspoilt treks past old tumbledown lengthmen's cottages, green crusty locks and wiers, and long silent mills.

West of England cloth had a reputation for being tough enough to stand up on its own and its single fault being that it never wore out. When the clothiers' trade was at its height contemporary writers speak of whole hillsides being red with cloth stretched out to dry on tenterhooks. Stroudwater scarlet was used for military and court uniforms as well as for hunting 'pink'. Uley was famous for its blues and woad and madder were grown to give the dyes.

White, yellow, black and green cloth (for billiard tables) were also woven, and before the mechanization of the nineteenth century practically every cottage in this agricultural district housed a spinning wheel and larger houses had looms.

When steam power came, the riots and machine-breaking incidents as well as the bankruptcy of some over confident mill-owners, sent the valleys into decline. The poverty was terrible and life was bleak until more resourceful mills gradually turned to other trades.

Firms began making paper and chemical dyes; woodworking mill-wrights started making pianos, walking sticks and furniture, and the iron side of the millers' business turned to foundry work and engineering. Some changed their enormous buildings into factories and food production like Hilliers, the bacon people at Nailsworth, and more recently smaller ones like Rooksmoor outside Stroud have become art galleries and shops.

There is a great feeling of continuity in the area and pupils take over from masters to such an extent that many of the original 'new' industries still thrive now in the 1980s.

Sim's Clock, Stroud.

Whilst the valleys churned busily the town of Stroud became the main market town for surrounding villages.

The original centre of the town was The Cross at the top of the High Street – overlooked by a draper's and china shop – now it is a launderette and an amusement arcade – where the old main road came in from Bisley.

This was the meeting place for townsfolk, a place for their maypoles, their fortune-tellers and ox roasts. Nearby were the stocks, the blind house and the town pump.

In 1607 a charter granted a regular Friday market and it was held in the space outside the churchyard. Here a little earlier, the market hall had been built and as butchers used the market place it became known as the Shambles (Victorian hinged butchers' tables still hang outside the shops).

Used for butter and poultry the market hall has had many additions and alterations and the façade is an interesting muddle of oriel window, Tudor arches and great propping buttresses.

In the centre there are two badly weathered columns supporting two stone brackets. Originally these brackets had been grotesque faces. When they were first replaced, the even uglier faces were christened Chambers and Barter (the churchwardens responsible for the good work) by the town hooligans.

Eventually the ridicule forced the men to replace the heads by the plain blocks that are there today. Now the building is known as the Town Hall, the upper part used by the Council and below on Fridays the Women's Institute has a produce market.

At one time in the 1930s a market took place outside the Painswick Inn and back a hundred and fifty years or so a regular pig market took place in the High Street.

A Stroud historian tells a story of some good fat pigs being walked into town and penned up in the street. They had been taught by their owner to come for food at the sound of a bell, thus when the town crier sounded his bell nearby, they leaped over the hurdles and scurried back home to be fed!

Today marketing is a little more conventional and apart from stalls in the Shambles on Friday there is a little Wednesday and Saturday Spook market on waste ground in Threadneedle Street.

When merchants and clothiers came down to Stroud to make their fortunes they left big family houses, schools, charities and name places; at the top of the town Whitechapel and Piccadilly.

The expanding centre of the town shifted from the churchyard to the area around the Subscription Rooms. Built for the sum of £2500, the rooms were opened in 1834 to be used for balls, concerts, lectures and bazaars.

'So many and various were the occasions on which the rooms have been open to the public', writes a Victorian, 'that if all that has been done there could be detailed, it would go far to illustrate the social and public habits, tastes, business, amusements and character of the last forty years of this wonderful nineteenth century.'

Today it is still used for the same varied activities. Unfortunately Stroud has suffered at the hands of planners and developers who busied themselves in the 1960s and 70s and sitting as it does in an Area of Outstanding Natural Beauty at the foot of the Cotswolds, the people in power seem incredibly insensitive and short-sighted regarding its heritage.

Recurrent plans for bypasses and ring roads have left dreadful flattened areas (around the old Cross) and medieval buildings sadly rot, so you have to look hard to see Stroud's past.

In Lansdown – the site of the short-lived cattle market of the late 1880s – the art school and museum is an amazing fairy-tale like building of gothic turrets, different textured bricks and busts of important men. Part of it houses the town's small museum.

As to be expected there are wool trade artifacts and some lovely Roman altars. There is a curious 'rocking' hip bath circa 1900 (adding no doubt hilarity to the weekly wash) and a good collection of domestic pottery showing that Gloucestershire has a fine tradition to maintain. Above these showcases, an enormous life-size model of a Megalosaurus looks down from swamps and forests.

From the museum you can walk up through public gardens to the church.

Stroud's church was almost completely rebuilt in 1866 and the inside is rather dark and ornate, but the delapidated churchyard hides interesting monuments under the damp pines.

Badly weathered and in the most neglected western corner is the pyramidal tomb of Lieutenant Delmont. A recruiting officer for the Napoleonic Wars, he was killed in a dual that is thought to be the last one staged in England. Unfortunately the occasion was not a gallant defending of gentlemen's character, but a rather amateur affair with rusty pistols, badly tended wounds and a negligent nursemaid who administered disinfectant as medicine.

Quite near to Delmont's tomb is the steep-sided pile of stones in memory of John Hollings, mercer, banker and captain of the Loyal Stroud Volunteers. He seems to have been quite a provocative character around Stroud, well gossiped about and arousing men's anger. He is supposed to have called the bluff of one malevolent gentleman, who wished to live long enough to see Hollings 'safe underground'. By not having his coffin interred but covering it with the pile of stones, Hollings scored a final triumph.

Amongst these more notorious gentlemen there are many graves marked farrier, wheelwright, plumber, and solicitor, illustrating that Stroud, the country market town, expanded to accommodate the needs of the business era.

Above the town the castellated folly of Rodborough Fort which now accommodates a caravan holiday site looks out over Selsey Hill and beyond to the glittering Severn.

Further on past the old carriers' stabling inn at The Bear the land opens out into a big plateau ridged by ancient earthworks and dotted with cattle and horses.

All around the edge of Minchinhampton Common there are marvellous views into other valleys and across to other hilltops and in the summer the turf is covered with cars, kites, ice-cream vans and golfers.

The rights of the Commoners (those living within the parish boundaries which now include Captain Mark Phillips) allow the grazing of cattle or horses for forty-six weeks a year. In April the Common is closed as the end of grazing year and opened again on 13 May with Marking Day. This takes place at the New Lodge Inn in the middle. The 'Hayward' is in charge of the animals throughout the year and to make sure all the animals are 'official' the cows are given ear tags (a different colour each year) and the horses have their hooves branded – a heart shape with an 'H' for Hampton.

Under the turf of the plateau is beautiful hard grey building stone. But since the area has been owned by the National Trust the stone is no longer quarried. Beneath the stone the layer of yellow clay called Fullers Earth, which was dug and used in the preparation of cloth, throws up numerous springs and Well Hill and Forwood in the town of Minchinhampton are always noisy with water.

Minchinhampton was a centre for wool and yarn and important as an eighteenth century coaching centre, being near the busy turnpike road to London. Although there is no regular charter market today, the Women's Institute holds an excellent produce and food market in the big upstairs room of the Market House. Opening to the queues at 9.30 a.m., all the best is gone within half an hour.

On the other side of the Golden Valley (Queen Victoria's description when she passed through by train) the labyrinths of steep donkey paths and narrow tracks connect the cottages and houses of Chalford to the mills at the bottom.

Higher up on the flatter land is the village of Bisley. Once as important as Stroud, it has now settled into a quiet mixture of humble cottages and grand mansions.

There are no markets now but the church keeps up an old tradition of Dressing the Wells, probably of pagan origin. Seven springs gush out below Jaynes Court and every year on Ascension Day they are strewn with flowers and blossom (perhaps as offerings to the deity of the life-giving waters).

As it happens when spring is at its best, the rambling churchyard smells of wild garlic and new grass as the children of the village school gather for a short service before their procession. Led by the vicar, they are taken over to the schoolyard where pairs rush to pick up their appointed letter.

They proceed to the wells with a local Silver Band and when the letters and wreaths have been hung on the well head to spell 'Ascension' and the year, the younger children, clutching hot little poses and bouquets, come forward one at a time to throw them onto the water. Another hymn and the blessing and it is time for tea, leaving the wells suddenly quiet but very beautifully adorned with all the many flowers.

Old people can remember this day as one of great excitement; children from outlying Church of England schools were collected by farmers in well-scrubbed carts and taken to Bisley. They assembled in the schoolyard much as they do today and after the service and the Well Dressing finished the day with sports and refreshments before returning home in the carts.

Yet another Gloucester custom with flowers and children is held at Painswick, well-known for its famous yews. In September on the feast day of the church, the graveyard fills with people for the Clipping Ceremony. This is nothing to do with the trees and comes from the old word 'yclept', to embrace. The children of the town, wearing garlands of flowers and holding hands around the church, sway backwards and forwards touching the building and singing the Clipping Hymn, celebrating its dedication.

In the past, Feast Sunday was a boisterous affair, with wrestling matches in the streets. 'Puppy Dog' pies were served – a plum pie hiding a china dog in memory of a wiley landlord who is said to have served up cooked dog to hungry travellers.

Painswick was also a clothiers' town and one that has attracted potters and weavers over the last century. In August the Guild of Gloucestershire Craftsmen have held their very excellent exhibition in the Institute annually since 1938. Their standards are extremely high and some members have pieces in the Victoria and Albert Museum in London.

In contrast to the tightly knit centre, it is possible to meander along a network of steep high-banked lanes that surround Painswick. Wick Street, the original road to Stroud, passes beautiful old farm houses and to the north the tiny hamlet of Paradise is supposed to have been named by Charles I.

On Haresfield Beacon a couple of miles west, the country again opens out giving a wider view than the one from Rodborough.

From this windy point the Severn snakes across the plain under the dark Forest of Dean and the panorama is one of the most spectacular in the county.

Some of the tiny back lanes from Painswick can take you through to Birdlip and Crickley. The road joining these two steep routes has laybys and vantage points from which to see the city of Gloucester.

At night the lights of the approach roads to the city make a dead straight thread across the plain from the hills, following the course of the Roman Ermine Street.

Gloucester, county town and cathedral city, sprawls alongside the Severn, the river that determined its original settlement. The centre is busy with stations and traffic, its outskirts encircled by ring roads, trading estates and spreading suburbs.

Mr Taylor's butcher's shop, Minchinhampton.

From the ridges of hills around and from the water meadows to the west, the cathedral tower dominates the skyline although the pattern of the streets is a legacy from the Romans. The four main streets – Northgate, Southgate, Westgate and Eastgate – were the main routes into the walled medieval town.

When the Romans made it a fort in the first century the Britons had already used it as a fording point, and it gradually gained importance as one of the four main centres in Britain for retired legionnaires.

The Normans followed the Saxon kings in making it a place of importance and favourite with monarchs. Many monasteries and religious houses were established – Greyfriars and Blackfriars are still names of parts of the town – and priories were built at Llanthony and St Oswald.

Edward the Confessor started a custom of spending Easter at Winchester, Whitsun at Westminster and Christmas at Gloucester. Thus when William the Conqueror held council in 1085 and gave orders for the *Domesday Book*, it was from Gloucester.

The walled town became the splendour of England. William the Conqueror went on to restore the almost defunct Abbey of St Peter and Abbot Serlo laid the first stone in 1087. The abbey church became a cathedral, and the murder of Edward II made his tomb a place of pilgrimage. With this wealth they built a new choir.

Gloucester has always been a developing town so each century changes what has gone before, knocks down or alters, and you have to search for the original medieval town.

A few obvious buildings stand out immediately, the New Inn in Northgate Street and the timbered Fish and Chip Shop in Hare Lane, but in Westgate Street you have to look carefully for the narrow Maverdine Lane that is next to the garden shop. By peering upwards, beams, windows and beautiful rope-like carvings can be seen. During the Royalist Siege in 1643 Colonel Massey had his headquarters in this house.

Very good town trails are published by the Civic Trust in Gloucester and explicit maps and clear drawings point out an amazing amount of old churches, gates, follies and foundations that would otherwise go unnoticed between the enormous shop fronts and modern buildings.

Gloucester has one of the furthest inland ports in England and has officially been a port since 1580, although traders used the waterways long before that date. During the Middle Ages Bristol took trade away from the town because the Severn was a difficult and treacherous river to navigate, so at the end of the eighteenth century local merchants built the Gloucester and Berkeley Ship Canal to link the port with the Bristol Channel.

Meanwhile as trade prospered fashion tried to turn the town into a spa but this time Cheltenham was too close and far too competitive. Nevertheless fine big family houses were built around the spa in the park and it became a desirable residential area.

At the centre of a big agricultural district with the wealth of the Cotswolds to the north-east and the rapidly improving dairy lands of the Vale, Victorian Gloucester thrived. Businesses and shops were opened and many new public buildings erected until the world wars stopped the progress.

Unfortunately the town has since suffered at the indiscriminate hands of planners and developers and the list of valuable demolished buildings is too long.

Trying to ignore the obvious and quite ghastly new mistakes of this city – a dreadful cement walkway across Southgate Street, and some hideous new shop fronts – the docks, the cathedral and the markets are well worth visiting.

In the cathedral precinct there are many lovely houses, gateways and five medieval halls hidden amongst the buildings of the Green. The cathedral itself combines sturdy homely Norman piers with the soaring filigree perpendicular style that was especially designed for the monks' new choir in the first half of the fourteenth century. From the ambulatory you can see where the mason sawed the great Norman pillars through the centre and set in the new delicate stone screen. In the transepts flying arches and buttresses cross the aisles and pierce earlier stonework.

The apsidal east end was pulled down and a great stained glass window – the biggest in England – put in its place. A corridor passes behind this window linking either side of the nave. A curved passage because of the canted window, it amplifies sound and is known as the 'Whispering Gallery'. All this tremendous remodelling was done with the money brought by pilgrims visiting the tomb of Edward the Confessor.

The Benedictine monks who lived in the monastery buildings and worshipped in the cathedral added cloisters to the north side, and the Gloucester masons who had already shown their skills in the choir fifty years earlier continued their fine work.

Up the walls and over the ceilings they created networks of stone ribs in semi-circular fan shapes. Little recesses were made for writing desks, there was

These 'mercy seats' are hinged ledges and the monks could perch on them during the long standing services of their daily lives. The carvings, not generally seen, are often vigorous and bawdy and at Gloucester there are men fighting, deer stalking and grape harvesting, as well as fabulous monsters, elephants, mermaids and dragons.

It is hard to believe that the cathedral, one of the most beautiful in England and containing unique examples of ecclesiastical monuments and architecture, was in danger of demolition in the seventeenth century. Between 1652 and 1657 a syndicate was formed to bring about its destruction, but very fortunately, the Mayor and Corporation of the times were able to stop them and the building was saved.

Now throughout the year, architects and masons climb about the cathedral inspecting water levels and subsidence and checking the stone. Each pinnacle of the tower needs replacing every ninety years or so due to wind and rain, and hard winters and frosts gradually split the limestone blocks.

In the eighteenth and nineteenth centuries the towers and spires of Gloucester churches were joined on the skyline by the masts and riggings of sailing ships and barges. Contemporary writers note fleets of white sails winding up the wide Severn to the port, and old photographs show the dockside crammed with vessels.

When much trade was lost to Bristol and Avonmouth and big ships stopped at Sharpness despite the Gloucester and Berkeley Ship Canal the docks became quieter and now only Pridays Flour Mills remain. But the warehouses are fine high brick buildings and along with the Customs Houses and offices there are plans to rejuvenate the area with hotels, shops and offices.

The local arts trust already has a barge moored there and the Mariners' Chapel is still in use.

From the Llanthony bridge you can see the main basins and the quays – at the moment so authentic and unaltered that they are often used as film sets.

Bigger and more frequent comings and goings take place down at Sharpness, where a continual stream of cargo vessels unload timber or coal and load up with cereals or scrap iron.

Whilst the importance of Gloucester as a port has waned, its status as a market town has remained constant. There has been a market in the town since the time of King John (1199) although an actual charter reference did not appear until the sixteenth

The cloisters of Gloucester Cathedral, a quiet sun trap on a summer's day.

a washing place or lavatorium and a cupboard for the monks' towels. New lights have been fitted in the corridors which show up the beautiful work and very careful inspection will reveal bits that don't fit in this amazing fifteenth-century mass production. There is also an old game of fox and geese scratched on one of the stone benches that run along the walls.

In the middle of the cloisters the little garden is open to the public and to the right of the entrance there is a head as a finial to a low buttress. This is a likeness of Dean Seiriol Evans and put there in 1971 on his retirement. Being an inquisitive man knowing every stone of his cathedral, the stonemasons had to set up a little bit of scaffolding and drape the head with sacking, and pass it off as 'maintenance work' to prevent discovery before it was unveiled.

The medieval craftsman often worked in very difficult conditions. Wooden scaffolding was used, lashed together with rope and a permanent exhibition in the tribune tells the story of the building of the cathedral. They worked as well in wood as they did in stone and the misericords in the choir are delightful carvings of scenes from the Bible and domestic life.

century. In 1227, Henry III granted a fair to the Lord of the Manors at Barton and that has survived as a September sheep fair and pleasure fair.

Big towns had many market sites and varying market crosses, and records report at least six in Gloucester. The oldest was probably the High Cross where the four Roman roads met. It was marked by a tall stone pinnacle, with niches filled by statues of the town's royal benefactors, the whole enclosed by railings and topped with a ball and cross. It was removed when the streets got busier with carriages and carts in the 1700s.

What remains of the Kings Board that used to be the old fourteenth-century Butter Cross in Westgate Street is now in Hillfield Gardens. It was a small covered area with statues, Gothic arches and scenes from the Bible. There were also meat markets, wheat and barley markets and one selling fish and herbs in Westgate Street (perhaps a legacy from monastic days).

In 1856 a new Eastgate Market was opened to replace an earlier building and the entrance (all that remains) is a high structure with giant Corinthian columns supporting reliefs and very naturalistic carvings of produce. To the left of the arches are fish, crabs and lobsters; in the centre maize, pineapples, plums, peaches and apples, and to the right flying duck, wild fowl, pheasants and hares.

In 1933 the World's Fair newspaper reports 'The Eastgate front is an imposing one being of stone, and is supported by substantial Greek pillars. It is surmounted by a tower. The lower portion is entirely open between the pillars and magnificent wrought iron gates are used to close the market. Entering these gates the visitor is greeted with the sight of well-laden fruit and flower stalls which are succeeded by those of

Mariners' chapel, Gloucester Docks.

Bakers clock at the cross, Gloucester. On the hour the figures of Father Time, an Irish woman, a Scotsman and John Bull ring the bells.

a miscellaneous variety.' Some people remember it as a big draughty 'Paddington Station'.

As part of Gloucester's redevelopment in the sixties, the market building was demolished but the entrance retained for the new covered shopping precinct, and market premises behind were opened in 1968.

It is one of the most modern – and market officials report the cleanest – in the country. There are large storage areas above and below the ground floor and unique service corridors help the transporting of goods to the stalls.

In previous centuries animal markets were just held in the streets with portable pens but as Gloucester enlarged to become a major cattle market for the west of England, a permanent site was made where the bus station is now. Trees were planted and the whole area was very pretty and shady for the animals and farmers. It was exciting coming into the town to shop and find a

market day in full swing and the Kings Square and Market Parade noisy with mooing bleating beasts.

Originally the Corn Exchange was on the corner of Southgate Street but moved to be near the cattle market (and strangely in the twenties doubled as a *palais de danse* the rest of the week!)

The Second World War saw small animal markets disappear from many towns. Gloucester, being in a good position for the rest of the county and surrounding shires, opened a new progressive cattle market complex in 1955 which thrives, and is now reckoned to be the second largest in the country. Off St Oswald's Road, big, open hangar-like buildings house hundreds of pens and a series of swing gates near the truck bays makes unloading animals quick and easy. There are small auction rings with semi-circular viewing seats and it is entertaining to watch the heifers being hollered at and the imperceptible flick of wrists as bidding starts.

In the open sheds there are sheep and pigs and enormous boars with danger notices by their heavy concrete stalls. At ten o'clock on Mondays there is a produce auction and trestles are loaded with trays of hens' eggs and ducks' eggs, pats of bright farm butter, sacks of potatoes, green vegetables and pots of flowers.

The tumult and clammer of the main sheds gets louder as the pens fill up with pigs and sheep and the mothers and children and sightseers are joined by the farmers and the countryfolk. On Saturdays a large stall market lines St Oswald's Road and it is a popular shopping place with easy parking compared to the town.

Farming is now big business; modern scientific methods are used for rearing animals and growing crops, and buyers arrive at market in private aeroplanes. The old buildings of the last century – even those model farms the Victorians indulged in – are no longer practical, and new machinery requires bigger different-shaped barns and shelter sheds. Animal breeds have also been modernized. The Old Gloucesters were a local breed of cattle – brown beasts with a prominent white flash along the rump and tail – that produced creamy milk which the dairymaids turned into the famous Double Gloucester cheese. (Some of the farmhouses in the Gloucester and Berkeley Vales still have slatted cheese lofts and the old fashioned breeds of cattle and the long wooled Cotswold sheep can be seen in the summer at the annual Three Counties Show held at Malvern, Worcestershire.)

In the folk museum in Westgate Street there is a great copper vat that would hold eighty-five gallons of curds, as well as cheese presses and butter churns.

Industries in the town were numerous and varied. There were many pin-making factories and bells were cast in Gloucester for over seven hundred years, the Rudhalls being a famous bell foundry family. In their 150 years of bell making over five thousand bells were cast by the Rudhalls for churches and buildings in Great Britain. In the nineteenth century another local family, the Morelands, started a match factory, and the well-known 'England's Glory' matches were made in Bristol Road until 1976.

A whole room in the museum displays Severn fishing tackle with conical salmon putchers, nets and peculiar pronged forks for spearing eels. Lampreys are a primitive fish that feed by suckers and they used to be common breeders in the River Severn. They were great favourites with the Romans and when the kings of England began to spend Christmas in Gloucester they took an interest in the local speciality. As they were out of season in December and therefore a prized delicacy, the town began presenting a Lamprey pie to the resident king. All through the medieval period and the Civil War the tradition continued, often the privilege of making the pie falling to the same Gloucester family. Reforms of the nineteenth century abandoned the custom but revived it for Queen Victoria's birthday in 1893 and again for her Diamond Jubilee.

Pies have always been a very English form of cooking. Spectacular, elaborate and even gilded and painted, pies were popular in the sixteenth century, sometimes containing gunpowder surprises and live birds. Illustrations of the Gloucester lamprey pies show them as a legacy of these days, the high castellated crust decorated with crests and crowns, roses and heraldic animals.

The First World War stopped regular pies being presented to the monarchy and they are sent for special occasions only. Queen Elizabeth received one at her Coronation and one in 1977 for her Silver Jubilee.

There is a pub in Westgate Street called The Lamprey and further along the same street is a small museum devoted to Beatrix Potter, another regular visitor to Gloucester, who made parts of the town familiar to many children. As a young author staying near Stroud, she heard the story of John Prichard, a real tailor in Gloucester. He was commissioned to make a coat for the Mayor and on returning from a weekend away found his garment finished. He believed the fairies had done it, but in fact it had been completed by colleagues. Miss Potter altered the story slightly and made the helpful colleagues into industrious mice. Many of the illustrations are recognizable as parts of Gloucester, especially the tailor's house in College Court, Westgate Street. Now the shop relating to her story is full of books and china covered with Mrs Tiggywinkle and Peter Rabbit. Downstairs the tailor's kitchen has been reconstructed, whilst upstairs clockwork mice sew away at the embroidered waistcoat.

Warne and Co., the publishers, had had their eyes on the shop for years, but when it first became vacant, an antique dealer moved in. It was not until 1979, twenty-six years later that Percy's Antiques came up for sale and they were able to move in.

Produce at Gloucester cattle market.

In Gloucestershire many of the small market towns that missed being developed in the nineteenth century remain unspoilt, some with their original market buildings and, as the county is rich in traditions, many celebrating old customs year after year.

Over towards the Wiltshire border, **Tetbury** is a friendly country town where people stop to chat on street corners and traffic is more likely to be hay-strewn pick-ups and cattle trucks. Members of the royal family have lately moved to this part of Gloucestershire (and now there are three royal households quite near to Stroud).

Surrounded by good agricultural land, the town has had fairs and markets since the early fourteenth century. Whilst other communities floundered, Tetbury was prosperous enough in 1655 to pull down

the jumble of houses in the centre and build a splendid three-storey wool market house supported by fat Tuscan columns. (It is now slightly smaller, reduced to two storeys and the Butchers' Shambles pulled down.)

As with many successful market towns, trade spilled over to fill several market places and cars in the Chipping behind the White Hart Hotel are parked on the old cheese and bacon market. Despite this modern intrusion the elegance of the seventeenth and eighteenth centuries still makes the square charming and attractive – Georgian terraced houses on one side and a medieval street called Chipping Steps leads down to the present sheep and cattle market at the bottom of Gumstool Hill.

On Spring Bank Holidays the annual Wool Sack Race is held on this 1:6 gradient. Teams of men run up and down carrying half a hundred weight of wool – weighing more if it's wet – and this medieval show of strength is a popular day out. Crowds jostle amongst the street stalls during the day and sing and dance under the market house in the evening.

Tetbury lies on the edge of the easily worked and kindly limestone. The main roads are lined with gabled houses and porches, and sloping streets lead away from the market place to stone bridges over the stream-like River Avon.

From Bath Bridge you can see the Parish Church's tall spire and large Gothic revival windows. Inside are the peculiar corridors or 'cloisters' as they are locally known, that run around three sides, blocking any entrance to the nave, and you enter the body of the church via doors in the panelling that lead directly into pews.

On Fridays there is a Women's Institute market and it is a good chance to buy fresh home-made chutneys and cakes as well as taking a look at the interior of the market house. At the entrance hangs the old toll board and inside ancient sloping floors dip up and down between the wooden columns.

From Tetbury a straight road across the southern ridge of the Cotswolds decends sharply to the Severn Plain. The high skies and wide open spaces close, and tunnel into the beech woods covering the edge of the scarp.

Chipping steps, Tetbury. A medieval street lined with old cottages leads up to the original market place, although the market house stands away in the centre of the town.

Marvellous deep lanes wind down into **Wotton-under-Edge** and Dursley – in the spring white with anemonies and garlic scented, and in the autumn coppery yellow, dappled with light.

Both towns prospered as part of the woollen trade that developed the Stroud valleys. In the centre of Dursley stands an eighteenth-century market hall but the rest of the town has been taken over by Lister's Engineering Company.

Wotton is still much the 'praty market towne welle occupied with clothiers, having one faire long street' that Henry VIII described. There is a large wool church and several rows of attractive almshouses, medieval and Victorian Gothic.

As a town it is interested in its own history and the local societies and shop keepers organize an annual medieval Hey Day in May. The streets are closed to traffic and are filled instead with traders and Morris Dancers, and a sheep is roasted in the old market place.

The Town Crier also comes out and parades up and down in his frock coat, velvet breeches and tricorn hat. George Carpenter is a Wotton man who revived the old town custom in 1969 and now wins prizes at international competitions. Apart from festival days he can be seen on most Saturdays standing on a street corner bellowing out local news and events.

The latest historical addition to the town is a full-size replica of a Roman mosaic pavement – the largest north of the Alps. Locals have always known of the real Roman pavement hidden deep beneath the churchyard at Woodchester, a village near Stroud. When it was last unearthed (infrequently due to its delicate state) Bob Woodward, a Wotton builder, was so excited by it that he decided to attempt a copy so more people could enjoy it. With his brother John, they invented unique methods to put each of the 800,000 individually cut tessarae in their correct places and fill the gaps made by sixteenth century gravediggers. By chance the brothers had also purchased the Victorian Tabernacle Church in Wotton, complete with its congregational gallery. The floor turned out to be almost the exact size of the mosaic. After much patience and two and a half years' hard work the pavement replica is now open to the public from March to October.

On the ground floor display cases exhibit Roman coins and pottery – finds from nearby Kingscote, whilst upstairs the congregational gallery is now the public viewing area where you can look down on Orpeus resplendent with lyre and peacocks. A

The figure of Queen Anne high above the arches of Dursley Market House. The building still shelters a small weekly market despite the fact that it is totally encircled by roads and traffic.

fabulous procession of animals surround him – a tigress, a leopard, an elephant, a horse, a wild boar and a stag – and there is a head of Neptune sprouting lobster claws, and nymphs and birds, all encircled by a typical Roman scroll of Acanthus leaves.

The original pavement was made in circa AD 325 by craftsmen from the Corinium School of Mosaicists and tells the myth of Orpheus charming nature with his music.

The mosaic was first excavated properly in the eighteenth century by Samuel Lysons, a Gloucestershire antiquarian and by its grandeur it is believed to be part of a villa belonging to the governor of this western part of Roman Britain.

Wotton lies near to the border of the newly made County of Avon. In the centre of Avon is Bristol, thriving port and major city, and with several markets each day of the week as well as vast open ones on Sundays, it is too big to be included in this book.

To the east, between the M4 and the main roads to Bath and Chippenham there are tiny villages down the high-edged lanes.

Tormarton on the way to Marshfield has a stumpy church with a path shaded by an avenue of ancient yews. The simple nave is decorated with unusual circled and deeply carved capitals and vigorous zig-zags around the chancel arch. For a small church it has a fascinating collection of peculiar and macabre memorials and brasses to wealthy merchants.

Amongst the wooded coombes and hedge-lined fields, the stone town of **Marshfield** used to be the furthest tip of Gloucestershire and a shire stone marked the place where it met Somerset and Wiltshire. Now it is part of enlarged Avon and fortunately bypassed by main roads and motorways.

It was once a big malting town with vast sheep fairs in May and October, the good land around raising the animals and the barley. It stood on the direct route from Bristol to London and had a market as early as 1265. In the seventeenth century the main Bristol-Chippenham road also passed through the town and it developed as an important coaching place and the main street today is lined with fine houses, coaching inns and a milestone measures 103 miles to Hyde Park Corner.

The Catherine Wheel has a beautiful façade with an ornate parapet and the Tolzey or Town House, the old town's administrative headquarters, makes extremely grand public conveniences.

At the church end of the High Street there is an enormous empty tithe barn in the farmyard next to the Manor House and a circular dovecot can be seen over the garden walls.

The Market Place near the church is small and not big enough to hold the four or five thousand sheep that used to change hands at the two annual fairs, and at the turn of the century the fairs were moved to fields behind the town. But after the wars bigger towns like Bath and Chippenham took the trade, leaving Marshfield quieter and residential.

Prior to this the town would have been quite self-supporting with stores, shops and businesses. Shops were never self-service and you waited to be served perched on high bent-wood chairs. Some places had fascinating contraptions for giving change when the bill was paid. The money was put into an overhead cylinder, a handle pulled and it was spirited away to the cashier's booth in another part of the shop; another sharp tug and the cylinder came whizzing back with the correct change. Very exciting for bored

Mr Bodman's shop, Marshfield.

children shopping with their mothers.

There is a shop in Marshfield that has retained many of these old-fashioned things and is in fact a sort of museum. Bodman's grocery and drapery store is half way up the High Street, its windows advertising Hercules overalls and crammed with a mixture of old grocery packets and posters of local events.

A very upright blue-eyed Mr Bodman opens his shop every day as he has done for the last seventy or more years. On one side of the shop is the grocer's counter stacked with cornflake packets from the 1960s, old advertisements for Mansion polish, Fry's chocolate and Pears soap. Behind, tiny drawers are full of oriental spices and tapioca and sago. Balls of string hang above ready to tie up the parcels neatly in brown paper.

Across the wooden alleyway down the centre of the shop is the drapery department. Here are displays of old photographs of Mr Bodman's family and of Marshfield, an enormous horn gramaphone, and piles of dusty books.

The two parts were run very separately and the drapery assistant would not interfere with customers on the grocery side (although some fraternization must have gone on as in Mr Bodman's youth the draper girl and grocer boy left to get married). Mr Bodman has clear memories of fair days in Marshfield when there were rows of pigs in front of the 'Nelson' and sheep hurdled all the way up the High Street.

Although the fairs have now gone the Marshfield Mummers have revived this strange yuletide custom that lapsed like so many in the nineteenth century. The purpose of the costumes and the symbolism of the play – always a St George, and often a Father Christmas and a Doctor – have been lost in time but some think it represents the birth and death of nature.

The plays were rarely written down and Marshfield has been able to revive theirs simply because the vicar in the 1930s overheard his gardener reciting lines whilst working. As the family were interested in folklore, inquiries were made and research brought a Mummers group together again, based on the gardener's memories.

Called 'The Oldtime Paper Boys', they dress in costumes made from torn newspapers, and perform their play on Boxing Day. Starting in the Market Place they repeat the strange tableau and long speeches four times, finishing at the Almshouses at the end of the street.

The town is no longer a busy market centre, but the people have kept up the traditional spirit of this country town as well as making it a pleasant place in which to live.

Off the A46 Bath Road there is a turning to **St Catherine's.** An endless deep hollow lane with grass in the middle of the road and hedges of fern and hawthorn leads to a tiny Norman church set next to a big tithe barn and beautiful manor house.

Inside, the memorials to the local Strutts family are quite fantastic. Cool green and white decorated tiles are set into either side of the bell tower arch and over the chancel tiny mosaics – gold, red, rust, black and blue, tell the Ten Commandments and the Lord's Prayer.

Outside, the churchyard is lovely; unkempt and totally peaceful. Old tombs tilt lopsidedly, swamped with grasses and valerian; a very old rambling rose creeps over the porch and wild strawberries, bright red dots, are tucked into the cracks of the churchyard steps.

The terraced gardens of the big house next door seem quite unnaturally tidy and ordered by comparison and together the buildings form the perfect example of an English hamlet.

ADDITIONAL INFORMATION

Forest of Dean
Clearwell caves – open Easter to September, Tuesday, Wednesday, Thursday and Friday, Sunday and Bank Holidays, Tel. Cinderford 23700.
Dean Forest Railway Society at Norchard – open steam days in summer, small museum open summer Saturdays and Sundays.
Cinderford market day – Friday.
Tourist Information Office – The Library, Bellevue Road, Cinderford, Tel. (0594) 22581, and 6 College Street, Gloucester, Tel. (0452) 42118.
The Bread and Cheese Dole – after evensong on Whit Sunday at St Briavels.
Women's Institute market – Micheldean – Thursday 11.00 a.m. – 1.00 p.m. Coleford – Friday 10.00 a.m. – 12.00 p.m.

Frampton-on Severn
Frampton feast – August Bank Holiday or first Monday after 15 August.
Elver eating competition – Easter Monday.
Tourist Information Office (nearest) – 6 College Street, Gloucester, Tel. (0452) 421188.

Tewkesbury
Mop fair – September.
Market days – Wednesday and Saturday.
Tourist Information Office – 64 Barton Street, Tel. (0684) 295027.
John Moore Museum – open Easter to October, Tuesday – Saturday.
Early closing – Thursday.
Women's Institute market – Friday 9.45 a.m. – 11.30 a.m.

Winchcombe
Railway Museum – 23 Gloucester Street open Bank Holiday afternoons, Sundays in July and August, daily first week of August.
Winchcombe pottery – open most weekdays and Saturday morning.
No market
Tourist Information Office – Municipal Buildings, The Promenade, Cheltenham, Tel. (0242) 22878.

Chipping Campden
Dovers Hill Games – The eve of Spring Bank Holiday (May) (The Cotswold Olimpicks).
Scuttlebrook Wake – the following day.
Women's Institute market – Friday 9.45 a.m. – 11.00 a.m.
Tourist Information Office – Woolstaplers Hall Museum, High Street, Tel. (0386) 840289.
Early closing – Thursday.

Moreton-in-Marsh
Market day – Tuesday.
Early closing – Wednesday.
Tourist Information Office – Council Offices, Tel. (0608) 50881.
Women's Institute market – Thursday 10.00 a.m. – 11.30 a.m.

Stow-on-the-Wold
Stow fair – March, May, July, October 10.00 a.m. – 4.30 p.m.
Early closing – Wednesday.
No market
Tourist Information Office – The Library, St Edward's Hall, Stow, Tel. (0451) 30352.

Lechlade

Filkins Museum – open by appointment. Write to: Mr G Swinford, Cotswold, Filkins, Nr Lechlade, Glos. or telephone Mr Foster, Filkins 365.
Tourist Information Office – Corn Hall, Market Place, Cirencester, Tel. (0285) 4180.
Women's Institute market – Thursday 10.00 a.m. – 12.00 p.m.

Northleach

Mop fair – early October.
Tourist Information Office – Bristol House, High Street, Burford, Tel. (099382) 2557, or Stow-in-the-Wold Library, Tel. (0451) 30352.
Cotswold Countryside Collection –
House of Correction – open daily during summer months, Tel. Corinium Museum (0285) 5611.
Women's Institute market – Wednesday 10.a.m. – 11.30 a.m.

Cirencester

Market days – Friday – Women's Institute and antique market. Monday and Friday – stall market. Tuesday – cattle.
Craft market in Corn Hall – March to December, twice monthly, first and third Saturdays 10.00 a.m. – 4.30 p.m.
Tourist Information Office – Corn Hall, Market Place, Tel. (0285) 4180.
Corinium Museum – Park Street, Cirencester, open October to April. Tuesdays to Saturdays 10.00 a.m. – 5.00 p.m. Sunday 2.00 p.m. – 5.00 p.m. May to September – Monday to Saturday 10.00 a.m. – 6.00 p.m. Sunday 2.00 p.m. – 6.00 p.m. Tel. (0285) 5611.

Gloucester

Market days – covered Eastgate market open Monday to Saturday – cattle Monday and Thursday – St Oswald's Road – stalls Saturday – St Oswald's Road.
Women's Institute market – stall every day in Eastgate Market.
Tourist Information Office – 6 College Street, Gloucester, Tel. (0452) 421188.
Barton sheep fair – generally Thursday nearest 28 September with Pleasure Fair in Gloucester Park.

Carnival – end of July.
Folk Museum – 99-103 Westagate Street, weekdays 10.00 a.m. – 5.00 p.m.
City Museum and Art Gallery – Brunswick Road, open weekdays 10.00 a.m. – 5.00 p.m.
City Eastgate – May to September – Wednesday, Friday and Saturday 2.00 p.m. – 5.00 p.m.
Three Counties Show – Malvern, Worcestershire – three days in June.

Stroud

Market days – Wednesday, Friday and Saturday.
Stroud festival – October (literature, music, drama and the arts).
Women's Institute market – Friday 8.00 a.m. – 10.30 a.m.
Early closing – Thursday.
Tourist Information Office – Council Offices, High Street, Tel. (04536) 4252.
Minchinhampton Women's Institute market – Thursday 9.30 a.m. – 11.00 a.m.
Dursley market days – Thursday and Friday.
Early closing – Wednesday.
Nailsworth – Early closing Thursday.
Wotton-under-Edge – Hey Day in May – Town Crier most Saturdays – Early closing Wednesdays.
Tetbury market day – Friday Women's Institute only – Wednesday cattle (plus two monthly large sales).
Early closing – Thursday.
Tetbury Woolsack Races – Spring Bank Holiday.
Randwick Mop and Cheese Rolling – first Saturday in May.
Cranham feast – August.
Wotton Women's Institute market – Friday 8.00 a.m. – 11.00 a.m.

Marshfield

Mummers Play – Boxing Day.
Tourist Information Office – Emery Lane Car Park, Chippenham, Tel. (0249) 55864.
No market.

*'Home again, home again,
Market is done.'*

Traditional nursery rhyme

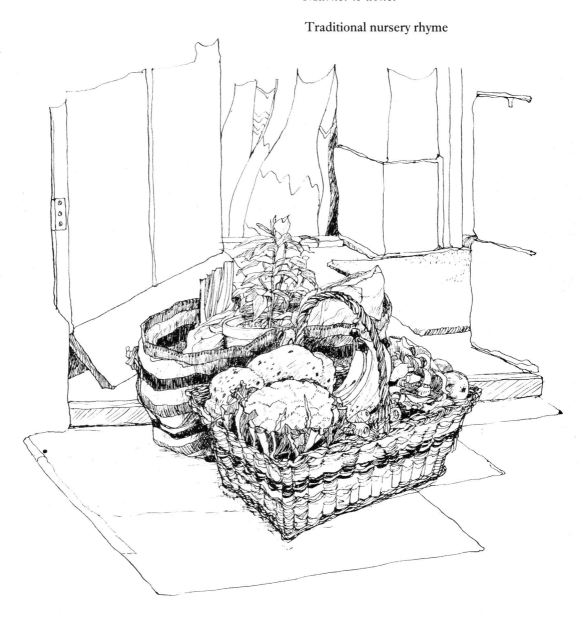

Selected Bibliography

The Market Traders Year Book, 1981, Worlds Fair (Oldham)

The Shell Country Alphabet, Geoffrey Grigson (Michael Joseph, 1966)

Life in a Medieval City, Joseph & Frances Giles (Arthur Barker, 1969)

The Old Roads of England, W. Addison (Batsford, 1980)

Old English Fairs, Rev. R.W. Muncey (Sheldon Press, 1936)

Pease & Chittys Laws on Markets & Fairs (Charles Knight & Co., 1958)

The Early Modern Town, edited by Peter Clark (Open University, 1976, Longman Group)

Markets and Fairs, J. Dorner (Wayland Publishers, 1973)

The History of the Woman's Institute – Inez Jenkins (O.U.P.)

Copies of the *Market Trader Newspaper Supplement to The Worlds Fair* (The Worlds Fair Ltd, Oldham, Lancs.)

English Markets and Fairs, William Addison (Batsford, 1953)

A Strong Land and a Sturdy, England in the Middle Ages, R. Barber (André Deutsch 1976)

English Traditional Customs, Christina Hole (Batsford, 1950)

The Drovers, Shirley Toulon (Shire Books, 1980)

Highways & Byways in Gloucestershire, Edward Hutton (Macmillan, 1932)

Highways & Byways in Somerset, Edward Hutton (Macmillan, 1912)

Highways & Byways in Wiltshire, Edward Hutton (Macmillan, 1919)

Highways & Byways in Oxford & the Cotswold, H.A. Evans (Macmillan, 1927)

The Kings England Series, edited by Aurther Mee (Hodder & Stoughton)

The Buildings of England, edited by Nikolaus Pevsner (Penguin Books)

The Victoria History of the Counties of England (University of London and Constable and Co.)

Hard Times in the Forest, Timothy Mountjoy (Forest of Dean Newspapers, 1971)

An Industrial Tour of the Wye Valley and the Forest of Dean, H.W. Paar (West London Industrial Archaelogical Soc., 1980)

Cotswold Stone, Freda Derrick (Chapman & Hall, 1948)

Industrial Archaeology in Gloucestershire, edited by Rev. Awdry (Glos. Society for Industrial Archaeology, 1970)

Cotswolds to Calais, Marian Woodman (Corinium Museum, 1981)

Winchcombe Cavalcade, Eleanor Adlard (J. Burrow & Co., London, 1939)

Minchinhampton & Avening, A.T. Playne (Alan Sutton, Glos., 1978)

A Good Plain Country Town, Ross 1800-1930, Fred Druce (Ivan Perry Ross, 1980)

Brief Guide to the Severn and its Bore, No.23, Fred Rowbottam (The Raleigh Press, 1967)

Fishing in the Lower Severn, John Neufville-Taylor (Glos. City Museums, 1974)

Gloucestershire, A Shell Guide, Anthony West (Faber & Faber, 1939)

Gloucestershire, The County Books Series, Kenneth Hare (Robert Hale)

Cotswolds, a New Study, Hadfield (David & Charles, 1973)

A Portrait of Gloucestershire, T.A. Ryder (Robert Hale, 1966)

History of Filkins, George Swinford (unpublished, 1955-6)

The Wotton Mosaic, R. Woodward & Rev. John Cull (Wotton Mosaics, 1981)

The Folklore of the Cotswolds, Katherine M. Briggs (Batsford, 1974)

The Secret Forest, Ray Wright (The Forest Bookshop, Coleford, 1980)

History of Bristol & Gloucestershire, Brian Smith & Elizabeth Ralph (Darwin Finlayson, 1972)

Companion into Gloucestershire, R.P. Beckinsale (Methuen, 1948)

A History of Tetbury, Eric Hodgson (Alan Sutton, 1978)

Wotton under Edge – E.S. Lindley (Museum Press, 1962)

History of Robert Dovers Olimpick Games, Francis Burns (Reliance Printing Works, Halesowen, 1981)

Royal Lamprey Pie of Gloucester, Robin Stayt & Patricia Gibson (Jennings, 1953)

Wootton Bassett, P.J. Gingell (Baileys Dursley, 1977)

A Portrait of Wiltshire, Pamela Street (R. Hale, 1971)

Savernake Forest, P.C. Walwin (privately published, 1976)

A History of Malmesbury, Dr Bernulf Hodge (Friends of Malmesbury Abbey, 1976)

Rollright Ritual, William Gray (Helios Books, 1976)

Wiltshire the County Series, Edith Oliver (R. Hale, 1956)

History of Chipping Norton, Eileen Meades (Alden Press, Oxford, 1949)

The Blanket Makers, A. Plummer & R. Early (Routledge & Kegan Paul, 1969)

History of Robert Dovers Olimpick Games, F. Burns (Reliance Printing Works, Halesowen, 1981)

Index